"HYMNAL SUPPLEMENT"

Code No. 840

AGAPE
Carol Stream, Illinois 60188

FOREWORD

The British Hymn Explosion of the '60's and '70's produced a wide variety of new hymns from a number of previously unknown authors and composers. Although it is still too soon to judge the significance of this happening, it is clear that the content andf style of hymn singing in the Christian Church has been fundamentally altered and that new directions are still emerging.

It all began with an emphasis on hymn texts in contemporary language speaking to the social issues of the day. Admittedly, many of these were of a transitory nature. The efforts of three pastors (Fred Pratt Green, Fred Kaan and Brian Wren), however, were more substantial in form and content and have become identified with the "Hymn Explosion."

The purpose of the HYMNAL SUPPLEMENT is to make available to American parishes and schools a number of the best of the hymns of these three, as well as others whose hymns have spread a song heard 'round the world. This includes the contributions of Timothy Dudley-Smith, Malcolm Williamson, Peter Cutts, Tom Colvin, Erik Routley, John Wilson, R. T. Brooks, David G. Wilson and Michael Baughen, as well as Canada's Margaret Clarkson. Although England seemed to be the place that, for the most part, spawned new hymn text writers, many American composers were active during this same period. Major U.S. contributors include the widely known hymns of Richard Avery and Donald Marsh. Works by the transplanted Britisher Alec Wyton, plus Richard Dirksen, Jane Marshall, Austin Lovelace, M. Lee Suitor, Carlton Young, John Ness Beck and Emma Lou Diemer also deserve mention.

Finally, some of these texts and tunes have undergone both minor or, in some cases, extensive alteration. Every effort has been made to have the author or composer provide any such changes so that the text and tune as they appear here should be considered the authorized (1984) version. No other changes in these hymns are permitted without the consent of the copyright holder. Permission to reproduce any of these hymns should be requested from the copyright proprietors whose names and addresses are listed in the index in the back of this hymnal.

THE PUBLISHERS

NEW SONGS OF CELEBRATION RENDER*

New songs of celebration render
To him who has great wonders done;
Awed by his love his foes surrender
And fall before the Mighty One.
He has made known his great salvation
Which all his friends with joy confess;
He has revealed to every nation
His everlasting righteousness.

Psalm 98, adapted by Erik Routley

*Hymn number 41, © 1974 by Agape.

When in Our Music God Is Glorified 1

1. When in our mu-sic God is glo-ri-fied, And ad-o-
2. How of-ten, mak-ing mu-sic, we have found A new di-
3. So has the Church, in lit-ur-gy and song, In faith and
4. And did not Je-sus sing a Psalm that night When ut-most
5. Let ev-ery in-stru-ment be tuned for praise! Let all re-

ra - tion leaves no room for pride, It is as though the whole cre-
men - sion in the world of sound, As wor-ship moved us to a
love, through cen - tu - ries of wrong, Borne wit-ness to the truth in
e - vil strove a - gainst the Light? Then let us sing, for whom he
joice who have a voice to raise! And may God give us faith to

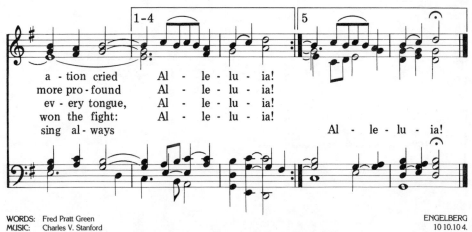

a - tion cried Al - le - lu - ia!
more pro - found Al - le - lu - ia!
ev - ery tongue, Al - le - lu - ia!
won the fight: Al - le - lu - ia!
sing al - ways Al - le - lu - ia!

WORDS: Fred Pratt Green
MUSIC: Charles V. Stanford

ENGELBERG
10 10.10 4.

2 We Meet You, O Christ

Unison

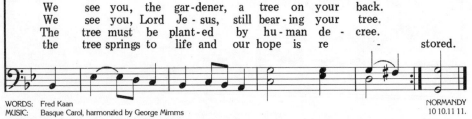

1. We meet you, O Christ, in man-y a guise:
2. In mil-lions a-live, a-way and a-broad;
3. We hear you, O Man, in ag-o-ny cry.
4. You choose to be made at one with the earth;

your im-age we see in sim-ple and wise.
in-volved in our life you live down the road.
For free-dom you march, in ri-ots you die.
the dark of the grave pre-pares for your birth.

You live in a pal-ace, ex-ist in a shack.
Im-pris-oned in sys-tems, you long to be free.
Your face in the pa-pers we read and we see.
Your death is your ris-ing, cre-a-tive your word:

1,2,3 | **4**

We see you, the gar-dener, a tree on your back.
We see you, Lord Je-sus, still bear-ing your tree.
The tree must be plant-ed by hu-man de-cree.
the tree springs to life and our hope is re-stored.

WORDS: Fred Kaan
MUSIC: Basque Carol, harmonzied by George Mimms

NORMANDY
10 10.11 11.

There's a Spirit in the Air 3

Flowing easily (♩. = c. 52-54)
Descant, Vs. 4 and 7 only

Praise   the love!   Praise   the love!

1. There's a   spir - it   in   the   air, tell - ing Chris-tians ev - ery-where:
2. Lose your shy - ness, find your tongue; tell   the world what God   has done:
3. When be - liev - ers break the bread, when a   hun - gry child   is   fed:
4. Still   his   Spir - it   leads   the fight, see - ing wrong and   set - ting right:
5. When   a   strang - er's   not   a - lone, where the home -less find   a   home:
6. May his   Spir - it   fill   our praise, guide our thoughts and change our ways.
7. There's a   Spir - it   in   the   air, call - ing peo - ple ev - ery-where:

Al - le - lu - ia!   Al - le - lu - ia!

**

Praise the love that Christ re -vealed,   liv - ing, work - ing   in   our world.
God   in Christ has come to stay.   We can see his   power to - day.
Praise the love that Christ re -vealed,   liv - ing, work - ing   in   our world.
God   in Christ has come to stay.   We can see his   power to - day.
Praise the love that Christ re -vealed,   liv - ing, work - ing   in   our world.
God   in Christ has come to   stay.   We can see his   power to - day.
Praise the love that Christ re -vealed,   liv - ing, work - ing   in   our world.

*Small notes for organ only.

WORDS: Brian Wren
MUSIC: John Wilson

LAUDS
77.77.

4 Jesu, Jesu, Fill Us with Your Love

Refrain
Unison

Je - su, Je - su, fill us with your love, show us how to serve the neigh-bors we have from you.

Fine

1. Kneels at the feet of his friends, si - lent - ly wash - es their feet, Mas - ter who acts as a slave to them.
2. Neigh - bors are rich and poor, neigh - bors are black and white, neigh-bors are near and far a - way.
3. These are the ones we should serve, these are the ones we should love. all are neigh-bors to us and you.
4. Lov - ing puts us on our knees, serv - ing as though we are slaves, this is the way we should live with you.
5. Kneel at the feet of our friends, si - lent - ly wash - ing their feet, this is the way we should live with you.

D.C.

WORDS: Tom Colvin
MUSIC: Ghana Folk Song, adapted by Tom Colvin, arr. by Jane Marshall

CHEREPONI
Irregular

Tell Out, My Soul 5

Unison

1. Tell out, my soul, the great-ness of the Lord! Un-num-bered
2. Tell out, my soul, the great-ness of his Name! Make known his
3. Tell out, my soul, the great-ness of his might! Pow'rs and do-
4. Tell out, my soul, the glo-ries of his word! Firm is his

bless-ings give my spir-it voice; ten-der to me the
might, the deeds his arm has done; his mer-cy sure, from
min-ions lay their glo-ry by. Proud hearts and stub-born
prom-ise, and his mer-cy sure. Tell out, my soul, the

prom-ise of his word; in God my Sav-ior shall my heart re-joice.
age to age the same; his ho-ly name, the Lord, the might-y one.
wills are put to flight, the hun-gry fed, the hum-ble lift-ed high.
great-ness of the Lord to chil-dren's chil-dren and for-ev-er-more!

WORDS: Timothy Dudley-Smith
MUSIC: Walter Greatorex

WOODLANDS
10 10.10 10.

6 God, Who Stretched the Spangled Heavens

1. God, who stretched the span-gled heav-ens, in-fi-nite in
2. Proud-ly rise our mod-ern cit-ies, state-ly build-ings,
3. We have ven-tured worlds un-dreamed of since the child-hood
4. As each far hor-i-zon beck-ons, may it chal-lenge

time and place, Flung the suns in burn-ing ra-diance through the
row on row; Yet their win-dows, blank, un-feel-ing, stare on
of our race; Known the ec-sta-sy of wing-ing through un-
us a-new, Chil-dren of cre-a-tive pur-pose, serv-ing

si-lent fields of space. We, your child-ren, in your like-ness,
can-yoned streets be-low, Where the lone-ly drift un-no-ticed
trav-'led realms of space, Probed the se-crets of the a-tom,
oth-ers, hon-'ring you. May our dreams prove rich with prom-ise,

share in-ven-tive pow'rs with you: Great Cre-a-tor,
in the cit-y's ebb and flow, Lost to pur-pose
yield-ing un-im-ag-ined pow'r, Fac-ing us with
each en-deav-or well be-gun: Great Cre-a-tor,

WORDS: Catherine Cameron
MUSIC: Franz Joseph Haydn

AUSTRIAN HYMN
87.87 7.D.

still   cre - a - ting,   show   us   what   we   yet   may   do.
and   to   mean - ing,   scarce - ly   car - ing   where   they   go.
life's   de - struc - tion   or   our   most   tri - umph - ant   hour.
give   us   guid - ance   till   our   goals   and   yours   are   one.

This Is the Threefold Truth 7

1. This   is   the   three - fold   truth   on   which   our   faith   de - pends;
2. Made   sa - cred   by   long   use,   new - mint - ed   for   our   time,
3. On   this   we   fix   our   minds   as,   kneel - ing   side   by   side,
4. By   this   we   are   up - held   when doubt   or   grief   as - sails
5. This   is   the   three - fold   truth   which,   if   we   hold   it   fast,

And   with   this   joy - ful   cry   wor - ship be - gins   and   ends:
Our   lit - ur - gies   sum   up   the   hope   we   have   in   him:
We   take   the   bread   and   wine   from   him,   the   Cru - ci - fied:
Our   Chris - tian   for - ti - tude,   and   on - ly   grace   a - vails:
Chang - es   the   world   and   us   and   brings   us   home   at   last:

Christ has   died!   Christ   is   ris - en!   Christ   will   come   a - gain!

WORDS: Fred Pratt Green
MUSIC: Jack Schrader

ACCLAMATIONS
12 12.12.

8 This Is My Father's World

1. This is my Fa - ther's world, and to my lis - ten-ing ears
2. This is my Fa - ther's world, the birds their car - ols raise,
3. This is our Fa - ther's world, O let us not for - get

All na - ture sings, and round me rings the mu - sic of the spheres.
The morn - ing light, the li - ly white, de - clare their Ma - ker's praise.
That though the wrong is great and strong, God is our Fa - ther yet.

This is my Fa - ther's world: I rest me in the thought Of
This is my Fa - ther's world: He shines in all that's fair; In the
He trusts us with his world, to keep it clean and fair, All

rocks and trees, of skies and seas his hand the won - ders wrought.
rust - ling grass I hear him pass, he speaks to me ev - ery - where.
earth and trees, all skies and seas, all crea - tures ev - ery - where.

WORDS: Maltbie D. Babcock, st 3 alt. by Mary Babcock Crawford
MUSIC: Malcolm Williamson

MERCER STREET
SMD

O God, Whose Will Is Life 9

1. O God, whose will is life and peace for all of your chil-dren,
2. O God, whose ways shall lead to peace, en-light-en us, we pray;
3. O God, who call-est us to peace, we join with ev-ery-one

let not our hu-man hates re-lease the sword's dread power a-gain.
dis-pel our dark-ness and in-crease the light a-long our way.
who does his part that wars may cease and jus-tice may be done.

For-give our nar-row-ness of mind; de-stroy false pride, we plead;
Il-lu-mine those who lead the lands, that they may make at length
En-a-ble us to take the way the Prince of Peace hath trod;

de-li-ver us and hu-man-kind from self-ish-ness and greed.
the laws of right to guide the hands that wield the na-tions'strength.
cre-ate the will to build each day the fam-i-ly of God.

WORDS: Rolland W. Schloerb
MUSIC: Thomas Tallis

THIRD MODE MELODY
CMD

10 Not to Us Be Glory Given

1. Not to us be glory given but to him who
2. Not what human fingers fashion, gold and silver,
3. Not in them is hope of blessing—hope is in the
4. Not the dead, but we the living praise the Lord with

reigns above: Glory to the God of heaven
deaf and blind, dead to knowledge and compassion,
living Lord! High and low, his Name confessing,
all our powers; of his goodness freely giving—

for his faithfulness and love! What though unbelieving
having neither heart nor mind— lifeless Gods, yet some adore
find in him their shield and sword. Hope of all whose hearts re-
his is heaven; earth is ours. Not to us be glory

voices hear no word and see no sign, still in
dore them, nerveless hands and feet of clay; still
vere him, God of Israel, still the same! God of
given but to him who reigns above: Glory

WORDS: Timothy Dudley-Smith
MUSIC: Rowland H. Prichard, harm. by Ralph Vaughan Williams

HYFRYDOL
87.87.D.

God my heart re - joic - es, work - ing out his will di - vine.
come, who bow be - fore them, lost in - deed and dead as they.
Aa - ron! Those who fear him, he re - mem - bers them by name.
to the God of heav - en for his faith - ful - ness and love!

Forgive Our Sins as We Forgive 11

Unison

1. "For - give our sins as we for - give," you taught us,
2. How can your par - don reach and bless the un - for -
3. In blaz - ing light your cross re - veals the truth we
4. Lord, cleanse the depths with - in our souls, and bid re -

Lord, to pray; But you a - lone can grant us grace to
giv - ing heart That broods on wrongs and will not let old
dim - ly know; How small the debts men owe to us; how
sent - ment cease; Then, rec - on - ciled to God and man our

live the words we say, To live the words we say.
bit - ter - ness de - part? Old bit - ter - ness de - part?
great our debt to you, How great our debt to you.
lives will spread your peace, Our lives will spread your peace.

WORDS: Rosamond Herklots
MUSIC: American Folk Tune, arr. by Austin C. Lovelace

DOVE OF PEACE
CM

Words used by permission of Oxford University Press.
Music Copyright © 1977 by Agape, Carol Stream, IL 60188. International Copyright Secured. All Rights Reserved.

12 Christ, upon the Mountain Peak

Unison

1. Christ, up - on the moun - tain peak stands a - lone
2. Trem - bling at his feet we saw Mo - ses and
3. Swift the cloud of glo - ry came, God pro - claim-
4. This is God's be - lov - ed Son! Law and pro-

in glo - ry blaz - ing; Let us, if we
E - li - jah speak - ing. All the pro - phets
ing in its thun - der him; Je - sus as his
phets fade be - fore him; First and last and

dare to speak, with the saints and an - gels
and the law shout through them their joy - ful
Son by name! Na - tions, cry a - loud in
on - ly one, let cre - a - tion now a-

praise him. Al - le - lu - ia!
greet - ing. Al - le - lu - ia!
won - der. Al - le - lu - ia!
dore him. Al - le - lu - ia!

WORDS: Brian Wren
MUSIC: Peter Cutts

SHILLINGFORD
7 8.7 8. Alleluia

Sing a New Song to the Lord 13

1. Sing a new song to the Lord, he to whom won-ders be-long! Re-joice in his tri-umph and tell of his pow'r— O sing to the Lord a new song!
2. Now to the ends of the earth see his sal-va-tion is shown; and still he re-mem-bers his mer-cy and truth, un-chang-ing in love to his own.
3. Sing a new song and re-joice, pub-lish his prais-es a-broad! Let voic-es in cho-rus, with trum-pet and horn, re-sound for the joy of the Lord!
4. Join with the hills and the sea thun-ders of praise to pro-long! In judg-ment and jus-tice he comes to the earth— O sing to the Lord a new song!

WORDS: Timothy Dudley-Smith; based on Psalm 98
MUSIC: David G. Wilson

CANTATE DOMINO
77.65.8.

14 You Are the Salt of the Earth

Slowly, strongly; a heavy two

You are the salt of the earth, he said, yes,

You are the salt of the earth. And you are the

light of the world, he said, yes, You are the light of the

WORDS and MUSIC: Richard Avery and Donald Marsh

CLARENCE
Irregular

4th time to Coda

world.

1. My fa-ther, my moth-er, my
2. So go share the fla-vor where-
3. So don't lose the sa-vor and

daugh-ter, my son, My sis-ter, my broth-er, yes,
ev-er you are, Give light like a lan-tern and
don't hide the light. For man-y are long-ing and

you are the one.
shine like a star.
lost in the night.

CODA

rit.

the world.

15 God of the Ages

Unison

1. God of the a - ges, His - to - ry's Mak - er,
2. God of this morn - ing, Glad - ly your chil - dren
3. God of to - mor - row, Strong O - ver - com - er,
4. Lord of past a - ges, Lord of this morn - ing,

Plan - ning our path - way, Hold - ing us fast,
Wor - ship be - fore you, Trust - ing - ly bow:
Princ - es of dark - ness Own your com - mand:
Lord of the fu - ture, Help us, we pray:

Shap - ing in mer - cy All that con - cerns us:
Teach us to know you Al - ways a - mong us,
What then can harm us? We are your peo - ple,
Teach us to trust you, Love and o - bey you,

Fa - ther, we praise you, Lord of the past.
Qui - et - ly sov - 'reign— Lord of our now.
Now and for - ev - er Kept by your hand.
Crown you each mo - ment Lord of to - day.

WORDS: Margaret Clarkson
MUSIC: Traditional Gaelic Melody, arr. by David Evans

BUNESSAN
10 9.10 9.

God, Whose Giving Knows No Ending 16

1. God, whose giv - ing knows no end - ing, from your rich and end - less
2. Skills and time are ours for press - ing toward the goals of Christ, your
3. Trea - sure, too, you have en - trust - ed, gain through pow'rs your grace con -

store: Na - ture's won - der, Je - sus' wis - dom, cost - ly cross, grave's shat - tered
Son: All at peace in health and free - dom, rac - es joined, the Church made
ferred; Ours to use for home and kin - dred, and to spread the Gos - pel

door, Gift - ed by you, we turn to you, of - f'ring up our - selves in
one. Now di - rect our dai - ly la - bor, lest we strive for self a -
Word. O - pen wide our hands in shar - ing, as we heed Christ's age - less

praise; Thank - ful song shall rise for - ev - er, gra - cious do - nor of our days.
lone: Born with tal - ents, make us ser - vants fit to an - swer at your throne.
call, Heal - ing, teach - ing, and re - claim - ing, serv - ing you by lov - ing all.

WORDS: Robert L. Edwards
MUSIC: C. Hubert H. Parry

RUSTINGTON
8 7.8 7.D.

17 God Who Spoke in the Beginning

Unison

1. God who spoke in the be - gin - ning, form - ing rock and
2. God who spoke through peo - ple, na - tions, through e - vents long
3. God whose speech be - comes in - car - nate— Christ is ser vant,

shap - ing spar, set all life and growth in mo - tion,
past and gone; show - ing still to - day his pur - pose,
Christ is Lord!— calls us to a life of ser - vice,

earth - ly world and dis - tant star; God who calls the
speaks su - preme - ly through his Son; God who calls the
heart and will to ac - tion stirred; God who us - es

WORDS: Fred Kaan
MUSIC: Erik Routley

CORBRIDGE
8 7.8 7.8 7.

Break the Bread, Jesus 18

Unison

1. Break the bread, *Je - sus, break the bread, and I shall
2. Pour the wine, Je - sus, pour the wine, and I shall
3. Give me love, Je - sus, give me love, and I shall

have a feast. I will break the bread, child, I will
have a feast. I will pour the wine, child, I will
have a feast. I will give you love, child, I will

raise the dead, child, and you shall have a feast.
make you mine, child, and you shall have a feast.
send the dove, child, and you shall have a feast.

*The word "Father" may be used instead of "Jesus."

WORDS: Herbert Brokering
MUSIC: Robert Wetzler

FEAST
Irregular

19 Now the Silence

Unison

Now the si - lence, Now the peace, Now the emp - ty hands up-
lift - ed; Now the kneel - ing, Now the plea, Now the Fa - ther's
arms in wel - come; Now the hear - ing, Now the pow'r,
Now the ves - sel brimmed for pour - ing;

WORDS: Jaroslav J. Vajda
MUSIC: Carl F. Schalk

NOW
Irregular

Now the bod - y, Now the blood, Now the joy - ful cel - e - bra - tion; Now the wed - ding, Now the songs, Now the heart for - giv - en leap - ing; Now the Spir - it's vis - i - ta - tion, Now the Son's e - piph - a - ny, Now the Fa - ther's bless - ing. Now. Now. Now.

20 Christ Is Made the Sure Foundation

With majesty (♩ = 84)

1. Christ is made the sure foun-da - tion, Christ the head and
2. All that ded - i - ca-ted cit - y, dear - ly loved of
3. To this tem - ple, where we call thee, come, O Lord of
4. Here vouch-safe to all thy ser - vants what they ask of

cor - ner - stone, Cho - sen of the Lord, and pre - cious,
God on high, In ex - ult - ant ju - bi - la - tion
hosts, to - day; With thy want - ed lov - ing kind - ness
thee to gain; What they gain from thee for - ev - er

f

bind - ing all the church in one; Ho - ly Si - on's help for-
pours per -pet - ual mel - o - dy; God the One in Three a-
hear thy ser - vants as they pray, And thy full - est ben - e-
with the bless - ed to re - tain, And here - aft - er in thy

ev - er, and her con - fi - dence a - lone; Ho - ly
dor - ing in glad hymns e - ter - nal - ly; God the
dic - tion shed with - in its walls al - way; And thy
glo - ry ev - er-more with thee to reign; And here-

WORDS: Latin 7th Century, trans. by John M. Neale
MUSIC: Richard Dirksen

CHRIST CHURCH (SYDNOR)
87.87.D.

Si - on's help for - ev - er, and her con - fi - dence a - lone.
One in Three a - dor - ing in glad hymns e - ter - nal - ly.
full - est ben - e - dic - tion shed with - in its walls al - way.
aft - er in thy glo - ry ev - er - more with thee to reign.

The Darkness Turns to Dawn 21

1. The dark-ness turns to dawn, the day-spring shines from heav'n,
2. The Son of God most high, be - fore all else be - gan,
3. God's Word of truth and grace made flesh with us to dwell;
4. How rich his heav'n-ly home! How poor his hu - man birth!
5. A ser-vant's form, a slave, the Lord con - sents to share;
6. O - be - dient and a - lone up - on that cross to die—
7. And still God sheds a - broad that love so strong to send

for un - to us a child is born, to us a Son is giv'n.
a vir - gin's son be - hold him lie, the new-born Son of Man.
the bright-ness of the Fa - ther's face, the child Em - ma - nu - el.
As mor - tal man he stoops to come, the light and life of earth.
our sin and shame, our cross and grave, he bows him - self to bear.
and then to share the Fa - ther's throne in ma - jes - ty on high.
a Sa - vior, who is Christ the Lord, whose reign shall ne - ver end.

WORDS: Timothy Dudley-Smith
MUSIC: Aaron Williams

ST. THOMAS
SM

22 How Wonderful This World of Thine

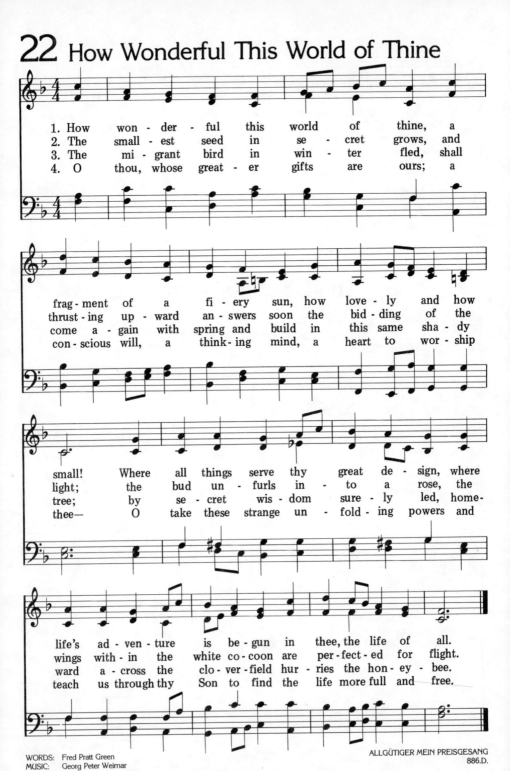

1. How won-der-ful this world of thine, a
2. The small-est seed in se-cret grows, and
3. The mi-grant bird in win-ter fled, shall
4. O thou, whose great-er gifts are ours; a

frag-ment of a fi-ery sun, how love-ly and how
thrust-ing up-ward an-swers soon the bid-ding of the
come a-gain with spring and build in this same sha-dy
con-scious will, a think-ing mind, a heart to wor-ship

small! Where all things serve thy great de-sign, where
light; the bud un-furls in-to a rose, the
tree; by se-cret wis-dom sure-ly led, home-
thee— O take these strange un-fold-ing powers and

life's ad-ven-ture is be-gun in thee, the life of all.
wings with-in the white co-coon are per-fect-ed for flight.
ward a-cross the clo-ver-field hur-ries the hon-ey-bee.
teach us through thy Son to find the life more full and free.

WORDS: Fred Pratt Green
MUSIC: Georg Peter Weimar

ALLGÜTIGER MEIN PREISGESANG
886.D.

Thanks to God 23

♩ = 100
Unison

1. Thanks to God whose Word was spo - ken in the deed that made the earth. His the voice that called a na - tion; his the fires that tried her worth. God has spo - ken:
2. Thanks to God whose Word in - car - nate glo - ri - fied the flesh of man. Deeds and words and death and ris - ing tell the grace in heav - en's plan. God has spo - ken:
3. Thanks to God whose Word was writ - ten in the Bi - ble's sa - cred page, Rec - ord of the rev - e - la - tion show - ing God to ev - ery age. God has spo - ken:
4. Thanks to God whose Word is pub - lished in the tongues of ev - ery race. See its glo - ry un - dim - in - ished by the change of time or place. God has spo - ken:
5. Thanks to God whose Word is an - swered by the Spir - it's voice with - in. Here we drink of joy un - mea - sured, life re - deemed from death and sin. God is speak - ing;

Praise God for his o - pen Word.

WORDS: R. T. Brooks
MUSIC: Peter Cutts

WYLDE GREEN
8 7.8 7.4 7.

24 Let Us Talents and Tongues Employ

Calypso rhythm, ♩ = 110
Unison

1. Let us tal-ents and tongues em-ploy, reach-ing out with a
2. Christ is a-ble to make us one, at his ta-ble he
3. Je-sus calls us in, sends us out bear-ing fruit in a

shout of joy: bread is bro-ken, the wine is poured,
sets the tone, teach-ing peo-ple to live to bless,
world of doubt, gives us love to tell, bread to share:

Christ is spo-ken and seen and heard.
love in word and in deed ex-press.
God-(Im-man-u-el) ev-ery-where!

Refrain
ff–mf

Je-sus lives a-gain,

ff–mf

WORDS: Fred Kaan
MUSIC: Jamaican Folk Song, adapted by Doreen Potter

LINSTEAD
L.M. Ref.

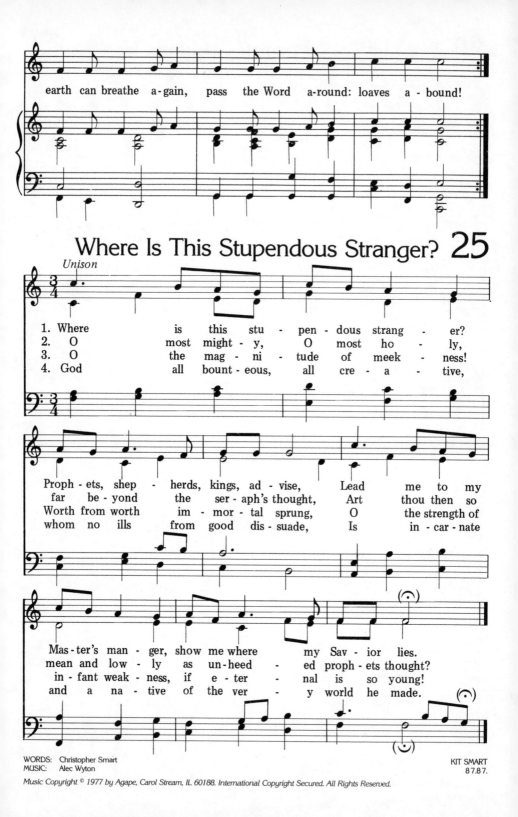

earth can breathe a-gain, pass the Word a-round: loaves a-bound!

Where Is This Stupendous Stranger? 25

Unison

1. Where   is   this   stu - pen - dous strang - er?
2. O   most might - y,   O   most ho - ly,
3. O   the mag - ni - tude of meek - ness!
4. God   all bount - eous, all cre - a - tive,

Proph - ets, shep - herds, kings, ad - vise,   Lead   me to my
far be - yond   the   ser - aph's thought,   Art   thou then so
Worth from worth   im - mor - tal sprung,   O   the strength of
whom no ills   from   good dis - suade,   Is   in - car - nate

Mas - ter's man - ger, show me where   my Sav - ior lies.
mean and low - ly   as   un - heed - ed proph - ets thought?
in - fant weak - ness, if   e - ter - nal is so young!
and   a   na - tive of the ver - y world he made.

WORDS: Christopher Smart
MUSIC: Alec Wyton

KIT SMART
87.87.

26 Glory Be to God the Father

Unison

Glo-ry be to God the Fa-ther, And to Christ his
on-ly Son. Praise we too the Ho-ly Spir-it,
Bind-ing hu-man-kind as one. As it was in
the be-gin-ning, Is for now and ev-er-more! A-
men, A-men! A-

WORDS: Gloria Patri, adapted by Carlton Young
MUSIC: Carlton Young

GLORIA PATRI
87.87.87. Ref.

men, A - men!

How Wondrous Great 27

Unison

1. How won - drous great, how glo - rious bright must
2. Our soar - ing spir - its up - ward rise to -
3. Our rea - son stretch - es all its wings, and
4. While all the heaven - ly powers con - spire e -

our Cre - a - tor be, Who dwells a - midst the
wards the burn - ing throne. There would we see the
climbs a - bove the skies; But still how far be -
ter - nal praise to sing; Let faith in hum - ble

dazz - ling light of vast e - ter - ni - ty.
bless - ed Three and the al - might - y One.
neath thy feet our ground - ling know - ledge lies!
notes a - dore the great mys - te - rious King.

WORDS: Isaac Watts, stanza 3 alt. by Caryl Micklem
MUSIC: Alec Wyton

SHORNEY
CM

28 There's a Church within Us, O Lord

Unison

1. There's a church with-in us, O Lord; There's a church with-in us, O Lord; Not a build-ing, but a soul, not a por-tion, but a whole; There's a church with-in us, O Lord.

2. There's po-ten-tial with-in us, O Lord; Some-thing stir-ring with-in us, O Lord; Some-thing strain-ing to have birth, to be vis-i-ble on earth, There's po-ten-tial with-in us, O Lord.

3. There's a fire with-in us, O Lord; A new life a-burn-ing, O Lord; A new fire for a life, com-bat-ting pres-ent strife, There's a fire with-in us, O Lord.

4. There's some build-ing to be done, O Lord; There's some build-ing to be done, O Lord; Not with steel, not with stone, but with lives which are your own, There's a church to be built, O Lord.

5. There's the church with-in us, O Lord; There's the church with-in us, O Lord; Not a build-ing but one soul, not a por-tion, but a whole, We are your church in the world.

WORDS and MUSIC: Kent Schneider

THE CHURCH WITHIN US
88.77.8.

You Called Me, Father 29

1. You called me, Fa - ther, by my name when I had
2. You give me free - dom to be - lieve; to - day I
3. With - in the cir - cle of the faith, as mem - ber
4. In all the ten - sions of my life be - tween my
5. So help me in my un - be - lief and let my

still no say; *to - day you call me
make my choice, and to the wor - ship
of your cast, I take my place with
faith and doubt, let your great Spir - it
life be true: feet firm - ly plant - ed

to con - firm the vows my par - ents made.
of the church I add my learn - ing voice.
all the saints of fu - ture, pre - sent, past.
give me hope, sus - tain me, lead me out.
on the earth, my sights set high on you.

(Alternative words where a person has not been baptized in infancy.)
*today, I come, commit myself, responding to your claim.

WORDS: Fred Kaan
MUSIC: Alice Parker

CONFIRMATION
CM

30 Though I May Speak with Bravest Fire

Unison

1. Though I may speak with brav-est fire,
and have the gift to all in-spire,
And have not love; my words are vain;
as sound-ing brass, and hope-less gain.

2. Though I may give all I pos-sess,
and striv-ing so my love pro-fess,
But not be giv'n by love with-in,
the prof-it soon turns strange-ly thin.

3. Come, Spir-it, come, our hearts con-trol,
our spir-its long to be made whole.
Let in-ward love guide ev-ery deed;
by this we wor ship, and are freed.

WORDS: Hal Hopson, based on 1 Corinthians 13
MUSIC: Hal Hopson, based on an American Folk Tune

GIFT OF LOVE
LM

Lord, Be Born in Our Hearts This Day 31

Unison

1. Lord, be born in our hearts this day, Holy
2. Lord, the world cries for u - ni - ty; bind our
3. Lord, be born in us ev - ery day, keep the

Spir - it, bring peace, we pray, Make the wars of the
hearts in com - mu - ni - ty, From all ha - tred our
world in your peace al - way, Ho - ly Spir - it, in

world to cease, Bring us, Lord, Christ - mas peace.
souls re - lease, Bring us, Lord, Christ - mas peace.
us in - crease, Bring us, Lord, Christ - mas peace.

Refrain

Christ - mas peace, Christ - mas peace, Bring us, Lord, Christ - mas peace.

WORDS and MUSIC: Richard Blank

CHRISTMAS PEACE
8 8.8 6. Ref.

32 All Who Worship God in Jesus

Unison

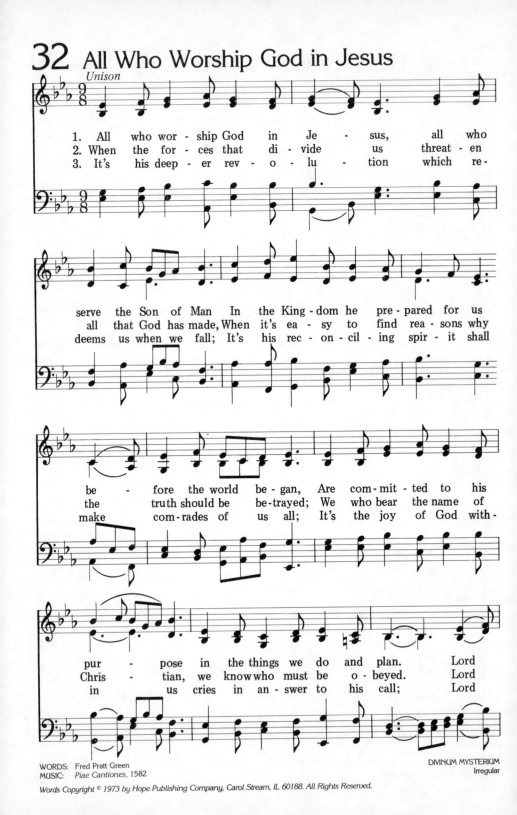

1. All who wor - ship God in Je - sus, all who
2. When the for - ces that di - vide us threat - en
3. It's his deep - er rev - o - lu - tion which re -

serve the Son of Man In the King - dom he pre - pared for us
all that God has made, When it's ea - sy to find rea - sons why
deems us when we fall; It's his rec - on - cil - ing spir - it shall

be - fore the world be - gan, Are com - mit - ted to his
the truth should be be - trayed; We who bear the name of
make com - rades of us all; It's the joy of God with -

pur - pose in the things we do and plan. Lord
Chris - tian, we know who must be o - beyed. Lord
in us cries in an - swer to his call; Lord

WORDS: Fred Pratt Green
MUSIC: *Piae Cantiones*, 1582

DIVINUM MYSTERIUM
Irregular

Je - sus, live in us!
Je - sus, live in us!
Je - sus, live in us! Live in me!

When Christ Was Lifted from the Earth 33

Unison

1. When Christ was lift - ed from the earth, his
2. Still east and west his love ex - tends, and
3. Where gen - er - a - tion, class or race di -
4. Thus free - ly loved, though ful - ly known, may

arms stretched out a - bove through ev - ery cul - ture,
al - ways, near or far, he calls and claims us
vide us to our shame, he sees not la - bels
I in Christ be free to wel - come and ac -

ev - ery birth, to draw an an - swer - ing love.
as his friends and loves us as we are.
but a face, a per - son and a name.
cept his own as Christ ac - cept - ed me.

WORDS: Brian Wren   BURLEIGH
MUSIC: Negro Spiritual, arr. by Harry T. Burleigh   CM

34 Christ Is Crucified Today

Sturdily, not too fast

1. Christ is cru - ci - fied to - day, Christ - mas is to - mor - row. Lent will fall in sum - mer - time, Eas - ter is to fol - low.
2. Christ is here and ev - ery - where, one with all his peo - ple, but we mark his where - a - bouts with our Sun - day steep - les.
3. Christ is Lord— we fence him out from rou - tine and Mon - day; tie him down to ho - li - ness, feast - ing, fast - ing, Sun - day.
4. Lord, for - give our for - mal ways and our spe - cial sea - sons; free us from the faith that stills, sti - fles, or im - pris - ons.
5. Make us whole and bind in one rea - son and e - mo - tion, let our life - style man - i - fest day - to - day de - vo - tions.
6. Give us grace to seize and use ev - ery sit - u - a - tion, an - y time for wor - ship, love, bless - ing, cel - e - bra - tion.

rit.

WORDS: Fred Kaan
MUSIC: Jane Marshall

NEW SEASON
7.7.7.7.

He Turned to Say, "Come, Follow Me" 35

Unison

1. He turned to say: "Come fol - low me."
2. I walked a - lone, I heard your cry.
3. My world was small, my neigh - bors few,
4. No for - eign kind, no a - lien race,

I joined his band to trav - el land and sea.
I came to you in - stead of pass - ing by.
But now God's love gives me a larg - er view:
In Christ we all have found a wel - come place.

And so we go to whom he sends, No long-er
We gave, we took; our sto - ry ends: No long-er
Be - fore the cross my world ex - tends, No long-er
The Spir - it binds, our voic - es blend; No long-er

strang-ers, we're sis-ters, broth-ers, friends.

WORDS and MUSIC: Richard Avery and Donald Marsh

COLLINS
Irregular

36 How Clear Is Our Vocation, Lord

1. How   clear   is our   vo - ca - tion, Lord, when
2. But   if,   for-get - ful,   we   should find   your
3. We   mar - vel how   your   saints   be - come   in
4. In   what   you give   us,   Lord,   to   do,   to -

once   we   heed   your   call: To   live   ac - cord - ing
yoke   is   hard   to   bear;   If   world - ly   pres - sures
hin-dranc - es   more   sure;   Whose   joy - ful   vir - tues
geth - er   or   a - lone,   In   old   rou - tines and

WORDS: Fred Pratt Green
MUSIC: C. Hubert H. Parry

REPTON
86.886.6.

37 Weary of All Trumpeting

WORDS: Martin Franzmann
MUSIC: Hugo Distler, adapted by Jan Bender

TRUMPETS
7 6.7 6.D.

That great　mu - sic pure and strong, where - with Heav'n　is　ring - ing.
In - to　your self - giv - ing death, call　us　all　to　fol - low.
Leav - ing　all, that we may be　part - ners　in　your splen - dor.

An Upper Room Did Our Lord Prepare 38

Flowing　　　　　　　　　　*Unison*

(Organ Introduction for Verses 1 & 4)

mp

1. An　Up - per　Room　did our
2. A　last - ing　gift　Je - sus
3. And　af - ter　Sup - per he
4. No　end there　is! We de -

senza Ped.　　　　　　Ped. ad lib.

Lord pre - pare　for those he loved　un - til　the　end: and his　dis -
gave his own:　to　share his bread,　his　lov - ing cup. What - ev - er
washed their feet,　for　ser - vice, too,　is　sac - ra - ment. In　him our
part　in peace. He loves be - yond　our　ut - ter - most: in　ev - ery

ci - ples still gath - er　there,　to　cel - e - brate their Ris - en Friend.
bur - dens may bow　us　down, he　by　his Cross shall lift　us　up.
joy　shall　be made com - plete—sent　out　to serve,　as　he　was sent.
room　in　our　Fa - ther's house he　will　be there,　as　Lord and Host.

WORDS:　Fred Pratt Green
MUSIC:　English Trad. Melody, arr. by John Wilson

FOLKSONG
9 8.9 8.

39 Let Us Build a House of Worship

1. Let us build a house of wor-ship to the God of heav'n and earth,
2. Let us build on God's foun-da-tion Je-sus Christ, whose blood a-tones;
3. Let us build to teach our chil-dren God's great glo-ry, power and grace;

where his church may bow be-fore him, hear his Word and sing his worth!
build with lives of grace and beau-ty, gold and sil-ver, pre-cious stones!
build to bring our friends and neigh-bors God's good news for all our race;

Not a-lone our bricks and mor-tar, hearts and lives to God we raise:
Let us build for now, for-ev-er; build for those who live to-day,
let us build to tell all na-tions life and health are theirs in God—

he will set his name for-ev-er on such build-ing to his praise.
build for fu-ture gen-er-a-tions truth that tri-umphs, come what may!
Je-sus Christ is Lord and Sav-ior! Sound his sav-ing name a-broad!

WORDS: Margaret Clarkson
MUSIC: Franz Joseph Haydn

AUSTRIAN HYMN
87.87 7.D.

I Come with Joy 40

Unison

1. I come with joy to meet my Lord, for - giv - en,
2. I come with Chris - tians far and near to find, as
3. As Christ breaks bread and bids us share, each proud di -
4. And thus with joy we meet our Lord. His pres - ence,
5. To - geth - er met, to - geth - er bound, we'll go our

loved and free, In awe and won - der to re - call his
all are fed, The new com - mun - i - ty of love in
vi - sion ends. The love that made us, makes us one, and
al - ways near, Is in such friend - ship bet - ter known; we
dif - f'rent ways, And as his peo - ple in the world, we'll

life laid down for me, his life laid down for me.
Christ's com - mun - ion bread, in Christ's com - mun - ion bread.
stran - gers now are friends, and stran - gers now are friends.
see and praise him here; we see and praise him here.
live and speak his praise, we'll live and speak his praise.

WORDS: Brian Wren
MUSIC: American Folk Tune, arr. by Austin C. Lovelace

DOVE OF PEACE
CM

41 New Songs of Celebration Render

1. New songs of cel - e - bra - tion ren - der to him who
2. Joy - ful - ly, heart - i - ly re - sound - ing, let ev - ery
3. Riv - ers and seas and tor - rents roar - ing, hon - or the

has great won - ders done; awed by his love his foes sur-
in - stru - ment and voice peal out the praise of grace a-
Lord with wild ac - claim; moun - tains and stones look up a-

ren - der and fall be - fore the Might - y One.
bound - ing, call - ing the whole world to re - joice.
dor - ing and find a voice to praise his Name.

WORDS: Psalm 98, adapted by Erik Routley
MUSIC: *Genevan Psalter*, 1543

RENDEZ A DIEU
98.98.D.

He   has   made known   his   great sal - va - tion
Trum - pets and or - gans   set in mo - tion
Right - eous, com - mand - ing, ev - er glo - rious,

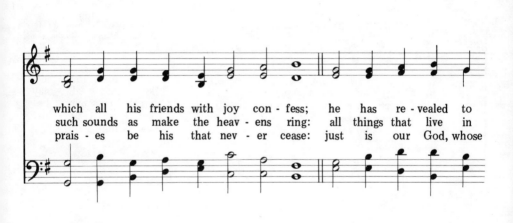

which all   his friends with joy con - fess; he has re - vealed to
such sounds as make the heav - ens ring: all things that live in
prais - es be   his that nev - er cease: just is   our God, whose

ev - ery na - tion his ev - er - last - ing right - eous - ness.
earth and o - cean make mu - sic for your Might - y King.
truth vic - to - rious es - tab - lish - es the world in peace.

42 May the Mind of Christ My Savior

1. May the mind of Christ my Sav - ior
2. May the word of God dwell rich - ly
3. May the peace of God my Fa - ther
4. May the love of Je - sus fill me,
5. May I run the race be - fore me,

live in me from day to day, By his love and
in my heart from hour to hour, So that all may
rule my life in ev - ery - thing, That I may be
as the wa - ters fill the sea; Him ex - alt - ing,
strong and brave to face the foe, Look - ing on - ly

power con - trol - ling all I do or say.
see I tri - umph on - ly through his power.
calm to com - fort sick and sor - row - ing.
self a - bas - ing, this is vic - to - ry.
un - to Je - sus as I on - ward go.

WORDS: Kate Wilkinson
MUSIC: John Wilson

GRIFFIN'S BROOK
87.85.

Now Let Us from This Table Rise 43

♩. = 42
Unison

1. Now let us from this ta - ble rise, re - newed in
2. With minds a - lert, up - held by grace, to spread the
3. To fill each hu - man house with love, it is the
4. Then grant us cou - rage, Fa - ther - God, to choose a -

bod - y, mind and soul; with Christ we die and
Word in speech and deed, we fol - low in the
sac - ra - ment of care; the work that Christ be -
gain the pil - grim way; and help us to ac -

live a - gain, his self - less love has made us whole.
steps of Christ, at one with all in hope and need.
gan to do we hum - bly pledge our - selves to share.
cept with joy the chal - lenge of to - mor - row's day.

WORDS: Fred Kaan
MUSIC: *Grenoble Antiphoner, 1753*

DEUS TUORUM MILITUM
LM

44 Great Is Thy Faithfulness

1. Great is thy faith - ful-ness, O God my Fa - ther, there is no
2. Sum-mer and win - ter, and spring-time and har - vest, sun, moon and
3. Par - don for sin and a peace that en - dur - eth, thy own dear

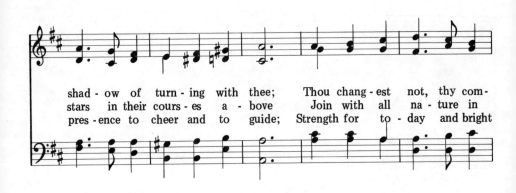

shad - ow of turn - ing with thee; Thou chang - est not, thy com -
stars in their cours - es a - bove Join with all na - ture in
pres - ence to cheer and to guide; Strength for to - day and bright

pas - sions they fail not; as thou hast been thou for -
man - i - fold wit - ness to thy great faith - ful - ness,
hope for to - mor - row, bless - ings all mine, with ten

WORDS: Thomas O. Chisholm
MUSIC: William M. Runyan

FAITHFULNESS
11 10.11 10. Ref.

Refrain

ev - er will be.
mer - cy and love. Great is thy faith - ful - ness! Great is thy faith - ful - ness!
thou - sand be - side!

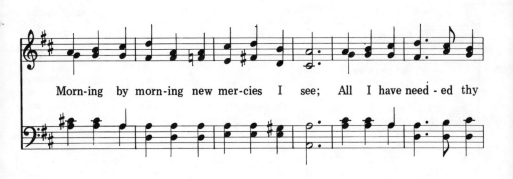

Morn-ing by morn-ing new mer-cies I see; All I have need - ed thy

hand hath pro - vid - ed— Great is thy faith - ful - ness, Lord, un - to me!

45 Lord, Who Left the Highest Heaven

1. Lord, who left the high-est heav-en for a home-less
2. Lord, who sought by cloak of dark-ness ref-uge un-der
3. Lord, who lived se - cure and set-tled, safe with-in the
4. Lord, who leav-ing home and kin-dred, fol-lowed still as
5. Lord, who in your cross and pas-sion hung be-neath a
6. Lord, who rose to life tri-um-phant with our whole sal-

hu-man birth and, a child with-in a sta-ble.
for-eign skies from the swords of Her-od's sol-diers,
Fa-thers plan, and in wis-dom, stat-ure, fa-vor,
du-ty led, sky the roof and earth the pil-low
dark-ened sky, yet whose thoughts were for your moth-er,
va-tion won: Ris-en, glo-ri-fied, as-cend-ed,

came to share the life of earth— With your grace and
rav-aged homes, and par-ents' cries— May your grace and
grow-ing up from boy to man— With your grace and
for the Prince of Glo-ry's head— With your grace and
and a thief con-demned to die— May your grace and
all the Fa-ther's pur-pose done— May your grace, all

WORDS: Timothy Dudley-Smith
MUSIC: German Trad. Melody, adapt. and harm. by William H. Monk

ALL SAINTS
87.87.87.

mer - cy bless all who suf - fer home - less - ness.
mer - cy rest on the home-less and op - pressed.
mer - cy bless all who strive for ho - li - ness.
mer - cy bless sac - ri - fice for right - eous - ness.
mer - cy rest on the help-less and dis - tressed.
con - flict past, bring your chil - dren home at last.

As We Break the Bread 46

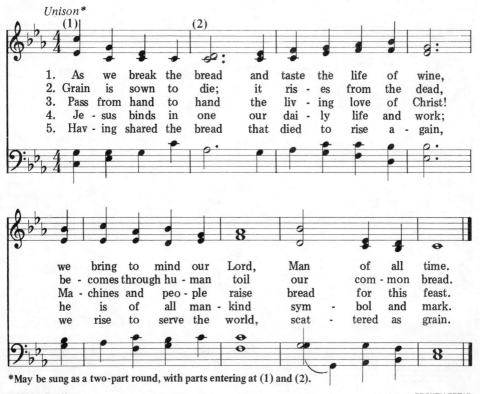

*Unison**

1. As we break the bread and taste the life of wine,
2. Grain is sown to die; it ris - es from the dead,
3. Pass from hand to hand the liv - ing love of Christ!
4. Je - sus binds in one our dai - ly life and work;
5. Hav - ing shared the bread that died to rise a - gain,

we bring to mind our Lord, Man of all time.
be - comes through hu - man toil our com - mon bread.
Ma - chines and peo - ple raise bread for this feast.
he is of all man - kind sym - bol and mark.
we rise to serve the world, scat - tered as grain.

*May be sung as a two-part round, with parts entering at (1) and (2).

WORDS: Fred Kaan
MUSIC: Patty Evans, harm. by Jane Marshall

BROKEN BREAD
56.64.

47 It Is God Who Holds the Nations

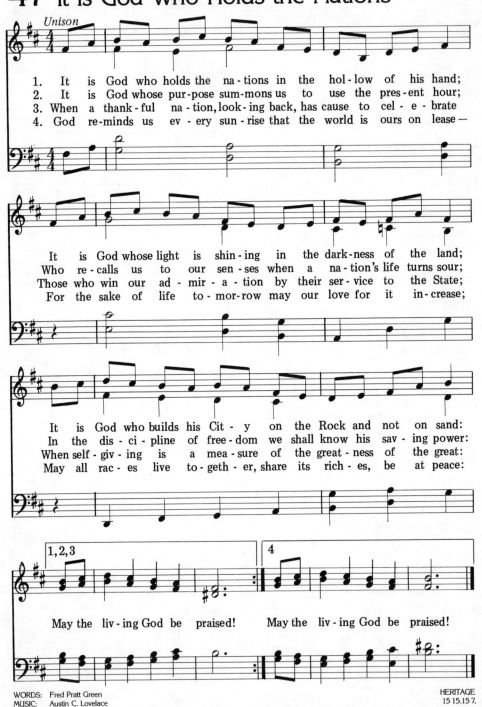

Unison

1. It is God who holds the na-tions in the hol-low of his hand;
2. It is God whose pur-pose sum-mons us to use the pres-ent hour;
3. When a thank-ful na-tion, look-ing back, has cause to cel-e-brate
4. God re-minds us ev-ery sun-rise that the world is ours on lease —

It is God whose light is shin-ing in the dark-ness of the land;
Who re-calls us to our sen-ses when a na-tion's life turns sour;
Those who win our ad-mir-a-tion by their ser-vice to the State;
For the sake of life to-mor-row may our love for it in-crease;

It is God who builds his Cit-y on the Rock and not on sand:
In the dis-ci-pline of free-dom we shall know his sav-ing power:
When self-giv-ing is a mea-sure of the great-ness of the great:
May all rac-es live to-geth-er, share its rich-es, be at peace:

1, 2, 3

May the liv-ing God be praised!

4

May the liv-ing God be praised!

WORDS: Fred Pratt Green
MUSIC: Austin C. Lovelace

HERITAGE
15 15.15 7.

Nature with Open Volume Stands 48

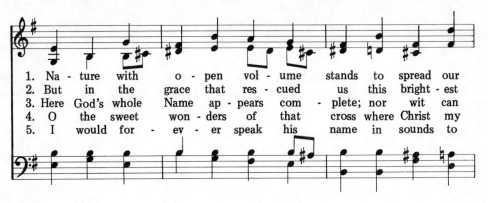

1. Na - ture with o - pen vol - ume stands to spread our
2. But in the grace that res - cued us this bright - est
3. Here God's whole Name ap - pears com - plete; nor wit can
4. O the sweet won - ders of that cross where Christ my
5. I would for - ev - er speak his name in sounds to

Mak - er's praise a - broad; And ev - ery la - bor from its
form of glo - ry shines; Here, on the cross, 'tis fair - est
guess, nor rea - son prove Which of the let - ters best is
Sav - ior loved and died! The no - blest life my spir - it
mor - tal ears un - known, With an - gels join to praise the

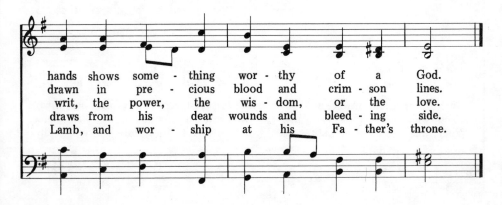

hands shows some - thing wor - thy of a God.
drawn in pre - cious blood and crim - son lines.
writ, the power, the wis - dom, or the love.
draws from his dear wounds and bleed - ing side.
Lamb, and wor - ship at his Fa - ther's throne.

WORDS: Isaac Watts
MUSIC: Melody by Nathanial Gawthorn, harm. by Samuel S. Wesley, ed. by Erik Routley

ELTHAM
LM

49 To Mock Your Reign, O Dearest Lord

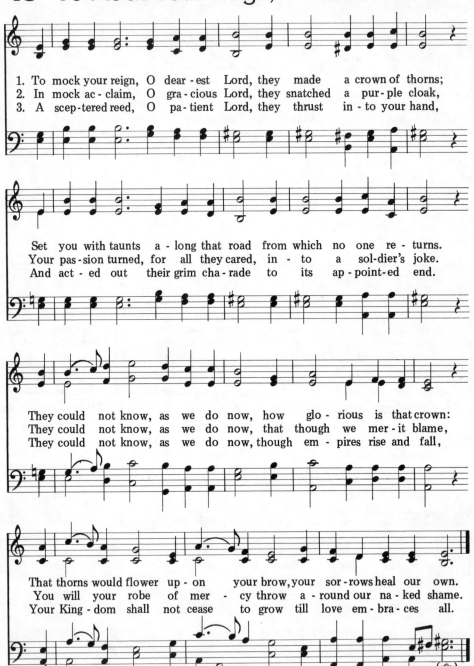

1. To mock your reign, O dear-est Lord, they made a crown of thorns;
2. In mock ac-claim, O gra-cious Lord, they snatched a pur-ple cloak,
3. A scep-tered reed, O pa-tient Lord, they thrust in-to your hand,

Set you with taunts a-long that road from which no one re-turns.
Your pas-sion turned, for all they cared, in-to a sol-dier's joke.
And act-ed out their grim cha-rade to its ap-point-ed end.

They could not know, as we do now, how glo-rious is that crown:
They could not know, as we do now, that though we mer-it blame,
They could not know, as we do now, though em-pires rise and fall,

That thorns would flower up-on your brow, your sor-rows heal our own.
You will your robe of mer-cy throw a-round our na-ked shame.
Your King-dom shall not cease to grow till love em-bra-ces all.

WORDS: Fred Pratt Green
MUSIC: Thomas Tallis

THIRD MODE MELODY
CMD

Lord Christ, The Father's Mighty Son 50

(Unison or Harmony)

1. Lord Christ, the Fa-ther's might - y Son, whose work up - on the
2. To make us one your prayers were said. To make us one you
3. Lord Christ, for-give us, make us new! What our de - signs could
4. We will not ques-tion or re - fuse the way you work, the

cross was done to give and re - ceive, make all our
broke the bread for all to re - ceive. Its piec - es
nev - er do your love can a - chieve. Our prayers, our
means you choose, the pat - tern you weave, but re - con-

scat - tered church - es one that the world may be - lieve.
scat - ter us in - stead: how can oth - ers be - lieve?
work, we bring to you that the world may be - lieve.
cile our war - ring views that the world may be - lieve.

*Small notes for organ only.

WORDS: Brian Wren
MUSIC: John Wilson

EAST MEADS
8 8 5.8 6.

51 O How Blessed Are the Poor in Spirit

Unison

1. O how blessed are the poor in spir - it, Theirs is the
2. O how blessed are the meek and hum - ble, They will in -
3. O how blessed are the mer - cy giv - ers, Such mer - cy
4. O how blessed are the true peace - mak - ers, They will be

King - dom of Heav-en. And how blessed are the sad and
her - it the earth. And how blessed those who hun - ger for
they will re - ceive. And how blessed are the pure in
known as God's chil-dren. And how blessed those who suf - fer for

Refrain

mourn - ful, They'll be con-soled by God.
good - ness, They all will feast with God.
heart, They sure - ly will see God.
jus - tice, They will be hon-ored by God. Blessed and hap - py

we shall be. Lis - ten to the Mas - ter's word!

WORDS and MUSIC: Richard Avery and Donald Marsh

THE BEATITUDES
9 8.9 6. Ref.

Soon the King-dom's com-ing, watch and see: the King-dom of the Lord!

Love Is Your Name 52

1. Love is your name, dear God of all, and
2. Love for the world which you have made, its
3. Love for man - kind, your im - age here, mat
4. Love for the Christ whose name we bear, his

love the ser - vice you de - sire. O - pen our ears to
life, its beau - ty and its wealth: Show us the du - ty
ter and spir - it one and free: Show us the child that
grace trans - form - ing all we do: Show us his pres - ence

hear your call, and light with - in us love's pure fire.
on us laid to guard its peace and serve its health.
you hold dear in ev - ery hu - man face we see.
ev - ery - where, that lov - ing all we may love you.

WORDS: R. T. Brooks
MUSIC: Johann H. Schein, harm. by J. S. Bach

EISENACH
LM

Words Copyright © 1984 in HYMNAL SUPPLEMENT by Agape, Carol Stream, IL 60188. All Rights Reserved.

53 Hail to the Lord's Anointed

Firm and martial

1. Hail to the Lord's a - noint - ed, great Da - vid's
2. He comes with suc - cour speed - y to those who
3. He shall come down like show - ers up - on the
4. Kings shall bow down be - fore him, and gold and
5. O'er ev - ery foe vic - to - rious, he on his

Organ *f (legato)*

great - er Son! Hail, in the time ap - point - ed,
suf - fer wrong, To help the poor and need - y,
fruit - ful earth, Love, joy and hope like flow - ers,
in - cense bring; All na - tions shall a - dore him,
throne shall rest; From age to age more glo - rious,

WORDS: James Montgomery
MUSIC: Malcolm Williamson

ANOINTED
7 6.7 6.D.

his reign on earth be - gun!
and bid the weak be strong;
spring in his path to birth:
his praise all peo - ple sing;
all bless - ing and all blest:

He comes to break op -
To give them songs for
Be - fore him on the
To him shall prayer un -
The tide of time shall

pres - sion, to set the cap - tive free;
sigh - ing, their dark - ness turn to light,
moun - tains shall peace, the her - ald, go;
ceas - ing and dai - ly vows as - cend;
nev - er his cov - e - nant re - move;

To take a -
Whose souls, con -
And right - eous -
His king - dom
His name shall

way trans - gres - sion, and rule in eq - ui - ty.
demned and dy - ing, were pre - cious in his sight.
ness in foun - tains from hill to val - ley flow.
still in - creas - ing, a king - dom with - out end.
stand for - ev - er, his change - less Name of Love.

54 The Church of Christ, in Every Age

1. The Church of Christ, in ev - ery age be - set by
2. A - cross the world, a - cross the street, the vic - tims
3. Then let the ser - vant Church a - rise, a car - ing
4. For he a - lone, whose blood was shed, can cure the
5. We have no mis - sion but to serve in full o -

change, but Spir - it - led, Must claim and test its
of in - jus - tice cry For shel - ter and for
Church that longs to be A part - ner in Christ's
fe - ver in our blood, And teach us how to
be - dience to our Lord; To care for all, with -

her - i - tage and keep on ris - ing from the dead.
bread to eat, and nev - er live un - til they die.
sac - ri - fice, and clothed in Christ's hu - man - i - ty.
share our bread and feed the starv - ing mul - ti - tude.
out re - serve, and spread his lib - er - a - ting Word.

WORDS: Fred Pratt Green
MUSIC: William Knapp

WAREHAM
LM

To a Maid Engaged to Joseph 55

Unison

1. To a maid en-gaged to Jo-seph, the an-gel Gab-riel came.
2. For you are high-ly fa-vored by God the Lord of all,
3. But Ma-ry was most trou-bled to hear the an-gel's word.
4. "Fear not, for God is with you, and you shall bear a child.
5. "How shall this be?" said Ma-ry, "I am not yet a wife."
6. As Ma-ry heard the an-gel she won-dered at his words.

"Fear not," the an-gel told her, "I come to bring good news,
who e-ven now is with you. You are on earth most blest,
What was the an-gel say-ing? It trou-bled her to hear,
His name shall be called Je-sus, God's off-spring from on high.
The an-gel an-swered quick-ly "The pow'r of the Most High
"Be-hold, I am your hand-maid," she said un-to her God,

Good news I come to tell you, good news, I say, good news."
you are most blest, most bless-ed, God chose you, you are blest!"
To hear the an-gel's mess-age, It trou-bled her to hear.
And he shall reign for-ev-er, For-ev-er reign on high."
will come up-on you short-ly, your child will be God's child."
"So be it, I am read-y ac-cord-ing to your Word."

WORDS: Gracia Grindal
MUSIC: Howard M. Edwards III

ANNUNCIATION
7 6.7 6.7 6.

56 Today I Live

1. To-day I live, but once shall come my death;
2. How I shall die, or when, I do not know,
3. When earth-ly life shall close, as close it must,
4. Mean-while I live and move and I am glad,

one day shall still my laugh-ter and my cry-ing,
nor where, for end-less is the world's ho-ri-zon;
let Je-sus be my broth-er and my mer-it.
en-joy this life and all its in-ter-weav-ing:

bring to a halt my heart-beat and my breath: Lord,
but save me, Lord, from thoughts that lay me low, from
Let me with-out re-gret re-call the past, then,
each giv-en day, as I take up the thread, let

give me faith for liv-ing and for dy-ing.
mor-bid fears that freeze my power of rea-son.
Lord, in-to your hands com-mit my spir-it.
love sug-gest my mode, my mood of liv-ing.

WORDS: Fred Kaan
MUSIC: Jane Marshall

HEARTBEAT
10 11.10 11.

When the Church of Jesus 57

Unison

1. When the Church of Je - sus shuts its out - er door,
2. If our hearts are lift - ed where de - vo - tion soars
3. Lest the gifts we of - fer, mon - ey, tal - ents, time,

lest the roar of traf - fic drown the voice of prayer:
high a - bove this hun - gry, suf - fering world of ours:
serve to salve our con - science, to our se - cret shame:

May our prayers, Lord, make us ten times more a - ware
Lest our hymns should drug us to for - get its needs,
Lord, re - prove, in - spire us by the way you give;

that the world we ban - ish is our Chris - tian care.
forge our Chris - tian wor - ship in - to Chris - tian deeds.
teach us, dy - ing Sav - ior, how true Chris - tians live.

WORDS: Fred Pratt Green
MUSIC: Ralph Vaughan Williams

KING'S WESTON
65.65.D.

58 Christ Is Coming

1. Christ is com - ing, Christ has come, let the world pre - pare a room. God says: Light! and makes our day: fear and cha - os lose their say. In our dark - ness shines our Sun;
2. Christ has come, will come a - gain, par - a - ble of God - and - Man. Lord of all our un - born days, world - re - new - ing turn of phrase, Word in sea - son for all time,
3. Let the earth make time and room for the Man who is to come. He, the cen - ter of our feast, makes him - self of all the least. Stones and voic - es all pro - claim:

WORDS: Fred Kaan
MUSIC: John Ness Beck

PREPARATION
7 7.7 7.7 7.

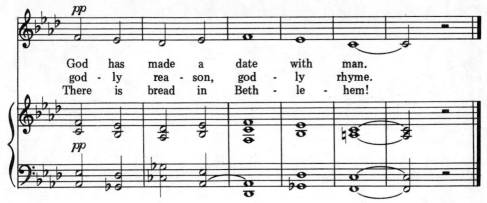

God has made a date with man.
god-ly rea-son, god-ly rhyme.
There is bread in Beth-le-hem!

Lord, You Give to Us 59

*Unison**

1. Lord, you give to us the pre-cious gift of life,
2. Lord, you give to us not on-ly flesh and blood,
3. Lord, you of-fer us the wa-ter, bread and wine.
4. Lord, you of-fer us new life that nev-er ends—
5. Lord, you ask of us a death to what we knew.
6. Lord, you share with us our hope for what will be.

Harmony (ad lib.)

a stew-ard-ship for ev-ery hus-band, ev-ery wife.
but mind and heart and soul to know that they are good.
By faith we reach to find your love with-in the sign.
you suf-fer, serve, and die, and live to call us friends.
Then, ris-ing in your name, we'll put our trust in you.
With us pre-pare each child by love, your love to see.

***In selected verses, measures 1-4 may be sung by men, women, or a soloist only.**

WORDS: Stephen Orchard
MUSIC: John Wilson

BINSCOMBE
5 6.12.

60 When the Lord in Glory Comes

Unison
Lively

1. When the Lord in glo-ry comes, not the trum-pets, not the
2. When the Lord is seen a-gain, not the glo-ries of his
3. When the Lord to hu-man eyes shall be-stride our nar-row

drums, not the an-them, not the psalm, not the
reign, not the light-nings through the storm, not the
skies, not the child of hum-ble birth, not the

thun-der, not the calm, not the shout the heav-ens
ra-diance of his form, not his pomp and power a-
car-pen-ter of earth, not the man by all de-

raise, not the chor-us, not the praise,
lone, not the splen-dors of his throne,
nied, not the vic-tim cru-ci-fied,

WORDS: Timothy Dudley-Smith
MUSIC: Michael A. Baughen, arr. by David G. Wilson

GLORIOUS COMING
Irregular

not   the si - lenc - es sub-lime,   not   the sounds of space and
not   his robe and   di - a - dems,   not   the gold and not the
but   the God who   died to save,   but   the vic - tor of the

time,   but his voice when he ap - pears   shall be
gems,   but his face up - on my sight   shall be
grave,   he it is to whom I fall,   Je - sus

mu - sic to my ears—   but his voice when he ap - pears   shall be
dark-ness in - to light—   but his face up - on my sight   shall be
Christ, my All in all—   he it is to whom I fall,   Je - sus

mu - sic to my ears.
dark - ness in - to light.
Christ, my All in all.

61 Earth and All Stars

1. Earth and all stars, loud rush-ing plan-ets Sing to the
2. Hail, wind and rain, loud blow-ing snow-storm Sing to the
3. Trum-pet and pipes, loud clash-ing cym-bals Sing to the
4. Ma-chines and steel, loud pound-ing ham-mers Sing to the
5. Class-rooms and labs, loud boil-ing test-tubes Sing to the
6. Knowl-edge and truth, loud sound-ing wis-dom Sing to the

Lord a new song! O, vic-to-ry, loud shout-ing
Lord a new song! Flow-ers and trees, loud rus-tling
Lord a new song! Harp, lute and lyre, loud hum-ming
Lord a new song! Lime-stone and beams, loud build-ing
Lord a new song! Ath-lete and band, loud cheer-ing
Lord a new song! Daugh-ter and son, loud pray-ing

Refrain

ar - my Sing to the Lord a new song!
dry leaves Sing to the Lord a new song!
cel - los Sing to the Lord a new song!
work - men Sing to the Lord a new song!
peo - ple Sing to the Lord a new song!
mem - bers Sing to the Lord a new song!

He hath done

mar - vel-ous things. I, too, will praise him with a new song!

WORDS: Herbert Brokering
MUSIC: David N. Johnson

EARTH AND ALL STARS
9 7.9 7. Ref.

O Jesus Christ, to You May Hymns 62

♩ = 120

1. O Je-sus Christ, to you may hymns be ris - ing,
2. Grant us new cour - age, sac - ri - fi - cial, hum - ble,
3. Show us your Spir - it, brood - ing o'er each cit - y,

in ev - ery cit - y for your love and care;
strong in your strength to ven - ture and to dare;
as you once wept a - bove Je - ru - sa - lem,

In - spire our wor - ship, grant the glad sur - pris - ing
To lift the fall - en, guide the feet that stum - ble,
Seek - ing to gath - er all in love and pit - y,

that your blest Spir - it rous - es ev - ery - where.
seek out the lone - ly and God's mer - cy share.
and heal - ing those who touch your gar - ment's hem.

WORDS: Bradford Webster
MUSIC: Daniel Moe

CITY OF GOD
11 10.11 10.

Words Copyright © 1954. Renewal 1982 by the Hymn Society of America, Texas Christian University, Fort Worth, TX 76129. Used by Permission. Tune and setting copyright Augsburg Publishing House. Used by Permission.

63 Glory Be to the Father

Glo - ry be to the Fa - ther, and the Son and the Ho - ly Ghost. As it was in the be - gin - ning, is now and ev - er shall be, World with - out end, A - men, As it was in the be - gin - ning, is

MUSIC: Richard Avery and Donald Marsh

PROCLAMATION
Irregular

64 Mary, Mary

Mar - y, Mar - y, what you gon - na name that ba - by?

What you gon - na call that ho - ly ba - by?

1. Slaves are we and look - ing for a mas - ter: Why don't you
2. We, like our sheep, need some - one to guide us, Why don't you
3. Hun - gry and poor, we need some - one to save us, Why don't you
4. Kings of the world, we seek some - one to rule us, Why don't you

1, 2, 3   **4**   *D.C. al Fine*

call him Lord? Sh! Let's all call him Lord!
call him Shep - herd? Sh! Let's all call him Shep - herd!
call him Sav - ior? Sh! Let's all call him Sav - ior!
call him King? Sh! Let's all call him   King!

WORDS and MUSIC: Richard Avery and Donald Marsh

ROSECHESTER
Irregular

I Lift My Eyes to the Quiet Hills 65

WORDS: Timothy Dudley-Smith
MUSIC: Michael Baughen and Elisabeth Crocker

UPLIFTED EYES
97.97.

66 A Mighty Fortress Is Our God

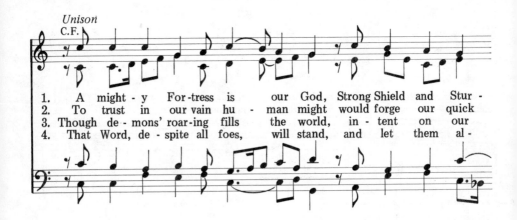

Unison
C.F.

1. A might - y For-tress is our God, Strong Shield and Stur -
2. To trust in our vain hu - man might would forge our quick
3. Though de - mons' roar-ing fills the world, in - tent on our
4. That Word, de - spite all foes, will stand, and let them al -

dy Wea - pon, Rock of de - fense and smit - ing Rod when
sur-ren - der. One Man wrings vic - tory from the fight, by
dam-na - tion, We scorn our fear and raise un - furled the
ways hear it! The Word stands by us, his strong hand sup -

C.F.

WORDS: Martin Luther, trans. by Samuel Janzow
MUSIC: Martin Luther, harm. by Richard Hillert

EIN FESTE BURG
87.87.66.66.7.

From CHURCH MUSIC, © 1970 by Concordia Publishing House. Used by permission.

C.F.

hordes of e - vil threat - en. Still fierce, our an - cient foe
God's choice our De-fend - er You ask me for His name?
ban - ner of sal-va - tion. The prince of dark - ness scowls,
plies his gifts and Spir - it. And if foes take by strife

wants on - ly our woe, Comes armed with brute might, de-ceit
Christ Je - sus, the same Who reigns on God's throne, Lord Sa -
un - ceas - ing - ly prowls. Fear not! his doom's sealed, for God
goods, fame, kin - dred, life, Then such be our loss, for we

and dead - ly spite. In God a - lone is res - cue.
ba - oth a - lone, He holds the field in tri - umph.
Him-self re -vealed The sim - ple Word that fells him.
still keep the cross, We hold the crown and king - dom.

8

67 Lift High the Cross

Refrain
Unison

Fine

Lift high the Cross, the love of Christ pro-claim, Till

all the world a-dore his sa-cred name.

Harmony

1. Come, Chris-tians, fol-low where our cap-tain trod, Our
2. Led on their way by this tri-um-phant sign. The
3. All new-born sol-diers of the Cru-ci-fied Bear
4. O Lord, once lift-ed on the glo-rious tree, As
5. So shall our song of tri-umph ev-er be: Praise

D.C. al Fine

king vic-to-rious, Christ, the Son of God.
hosts of God in con-qu'ring ranks com-bine.
on their brows the seal of him who died.
thou hast prom-ised, draw us all to thee.
to the Cru-ci-fied for vic-to-ry!

WORDS: George W. Kitchin and Michael R. Newbolt
MUSIC: Sidney H. Nicholson

By permission of Hymns Ancient & Modern.

CRUCIFER
1010.1010. Ref.

Long Ago, Prophets Knew 68

1. Long a-go, proph-ets knew Christ would come, born a Jew, Come to make all things new; Bear his Peo-ple's bur-den, Free-ly love and par-don.
2. God in time, God in man, This is God's time-less plan: He will come, as a man, Born him-self of wom-an, God di-vine-ly hu-man.
3. Ma-ry hail! Though a-fraid, She be-lieved, she o-beyed. In her womb, God is laid; Till the time ex-pect-ed, Nur-tured and pro-tect-ed.
4. Jour-ney ends! Where a-far Beth-l'em shines, like a star, Sta-ble door stands a-jar. Un-born Son of Ma-ry, Sav-ior, do not tar-ry!

Refrain

Ring, bells, ring, ring, ring! Sing, choirs, sing, sing, sing! When he comes, When he comes, Who will make him wel-come?
(last verse) We will make him wel-come!

WORDS: Fred Pratt Green
MUSIC: Melody from *Piae Cantiones*, 1582, arr. by Gustav Holst

THEODORIC
66.66.6. Ref.

69 Joy to the World

Unison

1. Joy   to   the world!   the Lord   is come;   let
2. Joy   to   the world!   the Sav - ior reigns;   let
3. No   more let sins   and   sor - rows grow,   nor
4. He   rules the world   with truth and grace,   and

earth re - ceive   her King;   Let   ev - ery heart   pre -
all   their songs   em - ploy,   While fields and floods, rocks,
thorns in - fest   the ground; He   comes to make   his
makes the na -   tions prove   The   glo - ries of   his

WORDS: Isaac Watts
MUSIC: Emma Lou Diemer

JOY
CM

pare him room, and heav-en and na - ture sing, And
hills and plains re - peat the sound - ing joy, Re-
bless - ings flow far as the curse is found, Far
right - eous-ness, and won - ders of his love, And

heav - en and na - ture sing, and heav-en and na - ture
peat the sound - ing joy, re - peat the sound - ing
as the curse is found, far as the curse is
won - ders of his love, and won - ders of his

1,2,3

sing.
joy.
found.

4

rit.

love.

rit.

70 Go Forth for God

Descant, Vs. 4 only

4. Go forth for God, go to the world in

Unison

1. Go forth for God, go to the world in
2. Go forth for God, go to the world in
3. Go forth for God, go to the world in
4. Go forth for God, go to the world in

joy, to serve God's peo - ple

peace; be of good cour - age,
love; strength - en the faint, give
strength; hold fast the good, be
joy, to serve God's peo - ple

WORDS: J. R. Peacey
MUSIC: Erik Routley

LITTON
10 10.10 10.

Words used by kind permission of Mrs. M. E. Peacey, widow of the author.
Music Copyright © 1984 in HYMNAL SUPPLEMENT by Agape, Carol Stream, IL 60188. All Rights Reserved.

ev - ery day and hour, and serv - ing

armed with heav'n - ly grace, in God's good
cour - age to the weak; help the af -
ur - gent for the right; ren - der to
ev - ery day and hour, and serv - ing

Christ, our ev - ery gift em - ploy, re - joic - ing

Spir - it dai - ly to in - crease, till in the
flic - ted; rich - ly from a - bove his love sup -
no one e - vil: Christ at length shall o - ver -
Christ, our ev - ery gift em - ploy, re - joic - ing

in the Ho - ly Spir - it's power.

king - dom we be - hold his face.
plies the grace and power we seek.
come all dark - ness with his light.
in the Ho - ly Spir - it's power.

71 Christ the Worker

LEADER:
Unison

1. Christ the work-er:

ALL:

1. Christ the work - er, born in Beth - le - hem, Born to
2. Bless - ed man - child, boy of Naz - a - reth, Grew in
3. Skill - ful crafts - man, bless - ed car - pen - ter, Prais - ing
4. Yoke mak - er, fash - ioned by his hands, Ea - sy
5. All who la - bor, lis - ten to his call, He will
6. Hea - vy la - den, glad - ly come to him, He will
7. Christ the work - er, love a - live for us, teach us

1-6 LEADER: · · **7**

work and die for ev - ery - one. (Bless - ed man - child:)
wis - dom as he grew in skill. (Skill - ful crafts - man:)
God by la - bor at his bench. (Yoke mak - er:)
yokes that made the la - bor less. (All who la - bor:)
make that heav - y bur - den light. (Heav - y la - den:)
ease your load and give you rest. (Christ the work - er:)
how to do all work for God.

WORDS: Tom Colvin
MUSIC: African Work Song, adapted by Tom Colvin

CHRIST THE WORKER
Irregular

Glory to God in the Highest 72

Broadly (♩ = c. 92)   *Unison*

1. Glo-ry to God in the high-est, re-joice in the
2. Wor-ship the Lord, the Al-might-y; de-vo-tion and
3. Je-sus, the Christ, the Re-deem-er, the Son of the
4. Christ and he on-ly is ho-ly, the Lord whose do-

praise of his worth! Glo-ry to God in the high-est, all
thank-ful-ness bring. 'Praise be to God for his glo-ry and
Fa-ther on high; led as a Lamb to the slaugh-ter, the
min-ion we own; one with the Fa-ther and Spir-it, most

crea-tures of heav-en-ly birth! Glo-ry to God in the
peace to his peo-ple', we sing; 'Glo-ry to God in the
Lord who was will-ing to die; God in the heav-en-ly
high, ev-er-last-ing, a-lone; reign-ing e-ter-nal in

high-est, and peace to his peo-ple on earth.
high-est, the Fa-ther and heav-en-ly King.'
plac-es, 'Have mer-cy up-on us', we cry.
glo-ry, the glo-ry of God on his throne. A-men.

WORDS: Timothy Dudley-Smith
MUSIC: Richard Proulx

RUSSWIN
8 8 8 8 8 8 8.

73 Thank You, God, for Water, Soil and Air

1. Thank   you, God,   for
2. Thank   you, God,   for
3. Thank   you, God,   for
4. Thank   you, ·God,   for
5. Thank   you, God,   for

wa - ter, soil and air—	large gifts sup - port - ing
min - er - als and ores—	the ba - sis of all
price - less e - ner - gy	stored in each a - tom,
weav - ing na - ture's life	in - to a seam - less
mak - ing plan - et earth	a home for us and

ev - ery-thing that lives.   For - give our spoil - ing and a - buse of
build - ing, wealth and speed. For - give our reck - less plun - der-ing and
ga - thered from the sun.   For - give our greed and care - less-ness of
robe, a frag - ile whole.   For - give our haste that tam-pers un - a -
a - ges yet un - born.   Help us to share, con - sid - er, save and

them.   Help us re - new the face of the
waste.   Help us re - new the face of the
power.   Help us re - new the face of the
wares.   Help us re - new the face of the
store.   Come and re - new the face of the

1, 2, 3, 4   **5**

earth.
earth.
earth.
earth.

                           earth.

rit.

74 Hope of the World

Unison

1. Hope of the world, thou Christ of great com-pas - sion:
2. Hope of the world, God's gift from high-est heav - en,
3. Hope of the world, a - foot on dust-y high - ways,
4. Hope of the world, who by thy cross didst save us
5. Hope of the world, O Christ, o'er death vic-tor - ious,

speak to our fear - ful hearts by con - flict rent.
bring - ing to hun - gry souls the bread of life:
show - ing to wan - d'ring souls the path of light:
from death and dark de - spair, from sin and guilt:
who by this sign didst con - quer grief and pain:

Save us, thy peo - ple, from con - sum - ing pas - sion,
Still let thy Spir - it un - to us be giv - en
Walk thou be - side us lest the tempt - ing by - ways
We ren - der back the love thy mer - cy gave us;
We would be faith - ful to thy Gos - pel glo - rious;

who by our own false hopes and aims are spent.
to heal earth's wounds and end our bit - ter strife.
lure as a - way from thee to end - less night.
take thou our lives and use them as thou wilt.
thou art our Lord! Thou dost for - ev - er reign!

WORDS: Georgia Harkness
MUSIC: *Genevan Psalter*, 1551

DONNE SECOURS
11 10.11 10.

*Words Copyright © 1954. Renewal 1982 by The Hymn Society of America, Texas Christian University, Fort Worth, TX 76129.
Used by Permission.*

O Father, You Are Sovereign 75

1. O Fa-ther, you are sov-ereign in all the worlds you made;
2. O Fa-ther, you are sov-ereign in all af-fairs of man;
3. O Fa-ther, you are sov-ereign, the Lord of hu-man pain,
4. O Fa-ther, you are sov-ereign! We see you dim-ly now,

your might-y Word was spo-ken and light and life o-beyed.
no powers of death or dark-ness can thwart your per-fect plan.
trans-mut-ing earth-ly sor-rows to gold of heav'n-ly gain.
but soon be-fore your tri-umph earth's ev-ery knee shall bow.

Your voice com-mands the sea-sons and bounds the o-cean's shore,
All chance and change tran-scend-ing, su-preme in time and space,
All e-vil o-ver-rul-ing, as none but Con-q'ror could,
With this glad hope be-fore us our faith springs up a-new:

sets stars with-in their cours-es and stills the tem-pest's roar.
you hold your trust-ing chil-dren se-cure in your em-brace.
your love pur-sues its pur-pose—our souls' e-ter-nal good.
our sov-ereign Lord and Sav-ior, we trust and wor-ship you!

WORDS: Margaret Clarkson
MUSIC: Melchior Teschner

ST. THEODULPH
7 6.7 6.D.

76 All Poor Men and Humble

1. All poor men and humble, all lame men who stumble, come
2. Though wise men who found him laid rich gifts around him, yet
3. Then haste we to show him the praises we owe him, our

haste ye, nor feel ye a-fraid;
ox - en— they gave him their hay:
serv - ice he ne'er can de - spise:

WORDS: English carol, trans. by K. E. Roberts
MUSIC: M. Lee Suitor

POVERTY
6 6.8.D.

For   Je - sus   our   trea - sure, with
And   Je - sus   in   beau - ty ac -
Whose love still is   a - ble to

love past all   mea - sure, in   low - ly poor
cept - ed their   du - ty; con - tent - ed in
show us that   sta - ble where soft - ly in

man - ger was   laid.
man - ger he   lay.
man - ger he   lies.

77 Glorious the Day

1. Glor - ious the day when Christ was born,
2. Glor - ious the day when Christ a - rose,
3. Glor - ious the days of gos - pel grace,
4. Glor - ious the day when Christ ful - fils,

Al - le - lu - ia, Al - le - lu - ia, Al - le - lu - ia!
Al - le - lu - ia, Al - le - lu - ia, Al - le - lu - ia!
Al - le - lu - ia, Al - le - lu - ia, Al - le - lu - ia!
Al - le - lu - ia, Al - le - lu - ia, Al - le - lu - ia!

To wear the crown that Cae - sars scorn,
The sur - est Friend of all his foes;
When Christ re - stores the fall - en race;
What self re - jects yet fee - bly wills;

Al - le - lu - ia, Al - le - lu - ia, Al - le - lu - ia!
Al - le - lu - ia, Al - le - lu - ia, Al - le - lu - ia!
Al - le - lu - ia, Al - le - lu - ia, Al - le - lu - ia!
Al - le - lu - ia, Al - le - lu - ia, Al - le - lu - ia!

WORDS: Fred Pratt Green
MUSIC: John Gardner

ILFRACOMBE
L.M Alleluias

Whose life and death that love re - veal,
Who for the sake of those he grieves,
When doubt - ers kneel and wa - verers stand,
When that strong Light puts out the sun,

Al - le - lu - ia, Al - le - lu - ia, Al - le - lu - ia!
Al - le - lu - ia, Al - le - lu - ia, Al - le - lu - ia!
Al - le - lu - ia, Al - le - lu - ia, Al - le - lu - ia!
Al - le - lu - ia, Al - le - lu - ia, Al - le - lu - ia!

Which we all need and need to feel.
Tran - scends the world he nev - er leaves.
And faith a - chieves what rea - son planned.
And all is end - ed, all be - gun.

Al - le - lu - ia, Al - le - lu - ia, Al - le - lu - ia!
Al - le - lu - ia, Al - le - lu - ia, Al - le - lu - ia!
Al - le - lu - ia, Al - le - lu - ia, Al - le - lu - ia!
Al - le - lu - ia, Al - le - lu - ia, Al - le - lu - ia!

78 For the Healing of the Nations

Unison

1. For the heal-ing of the na-tions, Lord, we pray with
2. Lead us, Fa-ther, in-to free-dom, from de-spair your
3. All that kills a-bun-dant liv-ing, let it from the
4. You, Cre-a-tor-God, have writ-ten your great name on

one ac-cord; for a just and e-qual shar-ing
world re-lease; that, re-deemed from war and ha-tred,
earth be banned; pride of sta-tus, race or school-ing,
hu-man-kind; for our grow-ing in your like-ness,

of the things that earth af-fords. To a life of
all may come and go in peace. Show us how through
dog-mas that ob-scure your plan. In our com-mon
bring the life of Christ to mind; that by our re-

love in ac-tion help us rise and pledge our word.
care and good-ness fear will die and hope in-crease.
quest for jus-tice may we hal-low life's brief span.
sponse and ser-vice earth its des-ti-ny may find.

WORDS: Fred Kaan
MUSIC: Carl F. Schalk

FORTUNATUS NEW
8 7.8 7.8 7.

1. A new day bids us wake to clear or cloud-y
(2. As) all life needs the sun, which nev - er ceas - es
(3. Once) more we rise to face an - oth - er day's be -
(4. So) now, in sol - i - tude, or met in Christ to -

weath - er, And for each oth - er's sake re
giv - ing, E - ven when day is done, its
gin - ning, To find in God's free grace for -
geth - er, We praise our liv - ing God, and

stores us to each oth - er: Re - mem - b'ring God, we say:
en - er - gy for liv - ing: For - get God though we may,
give - ness for our sin - ning: Re - sist God though we may,
pray for one an - oth - er: Be - liev - ing, come what may,

1, 2, 3 *rit.* **4**

This is God's world, God's day.
This is God's world, God's day. 2. As
This is God's world, God's day. 3. Once
This is God's world, God's day. 4. So
This is God's world, God's day.

WORDS: Fred Pratt Green
MUSIC: Carlton Young
GREEN
67.67.66.

80 Breathe on Me, Breath of God

mf (each time louder)

1. Breathe on me, breath of God, fill me with life a-new,
2. Breathe on me, breath of God, un-til my heart is pure,
3. Breathe on me, breath of God, till I am whol-ly thine,
4. Breathe on me, breath of God, so I shall ne-ver die;

That I may love what thou dost love, and do what thou
Un-til with thee I will one will, to do or to
Till all this earth-ly part of me glows with the light
But live with thee the per-fect life of thine e-ter-

would do. Breathe on me, breath of God.
en-dure. Breathe on me, breath of God.
di-vine. Breathe on me, breath of God.
ni-ty. Breathe on me, breath of God.

WORDS: Edwin Hatch
MUSIC: Malcolm Williamson

BREATH
SM Ref.

Christ Is Alive! 81

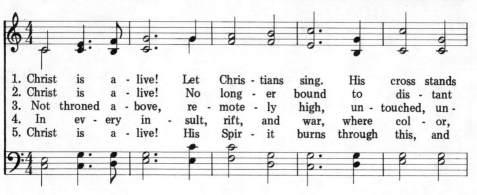

1. Christ is a - live! Let Chris - tians sing. His cross stands
2. Christ is a - live! No long - er bound to dis - tant
3. Not throned a - bove, re - mote - ly high, un - touched, un -
4. In ev - ery in - sult, rift, and war, where col - or,
5. Christ is a - live! His Spir - it burns through this, and

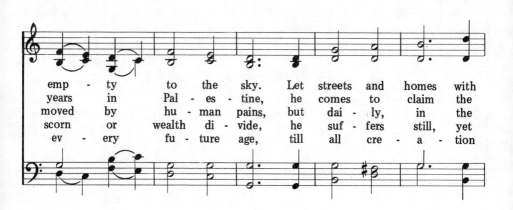

emp - ty to the sky. Let streets and homes with
years in Pal - es - tine, he comes to claim the
moved by hu - man pains, but dai - ly, in the
scorn or wealth di - vide, he suf - fers still, yet
ev - ery fu - ture age, till all cre - a - tion

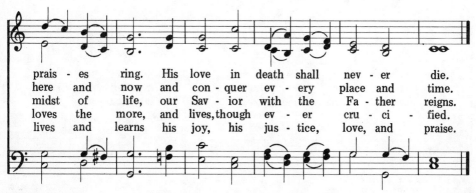

prais - es ring. His love in death shall nev - er die.
here and now and con - quer ev - ery place and time.
midst of life, our Sav - ior with the Fa - ther reigns.
loves the more, and lives, though ev - er cru - ci - fied.
lives and learns his joy, his jus - tice, love, and praise.

WORDS: Brian Wren
MUSIC: Thomas Williams *Psalmodia Evangelica*, 1789

TRURO
LM

82 As Water to the Thirsty

Unison

1. As wa-ter to the thirst-y, as beau-ty to the eyes, as
2. Like calm in place of clam-or, like peace that fol-lows pain, like
3. As sleep that fol-lows fe-ver, as gold in-stead of grey, as

strength that fol-lows weak-ness, as truth in-stead of lies, as
meet-ing af-ter part-ing, like sun-shine af-ter rain, like
free-dom af-ter bond-age, as sun-rise to the day, as

song-time and spring-time and sum-mer-time to be, so
moon-light and star-light and sun-light on the sea, so
home to the trav-'ler and all we long to see, so

is my Lord, my liv-ing Lord, so is my Lord to me.
is my Lord, my liv-ing Lord, so is my Lord to me.
is my Lord, my liv-ing Lord, so is my Lord to me.

WORDS: Timothy Dudley-Smith
MUSIC: T. Brian Coleman

OASIS
76.76.66.86.

By Gracious Powers 83

1. By gra - cious powers so won - der - ful - ly shel - ter'd,
2. Yet is this heart by its old foe tor - ment - ed,
3. And when this cup you give is filled to brim - ming
4. Yet when a - gain in this same world you give us

and con - fi - dent - ly wait - ing come what may,
still e - vil days bring bur - dens hard to bear;
with bit - ter sor - row, hard to un - der - stand,
the joy we had, the bright - ness of your Sun,

We know that God is with us night and morn - ing,
O give our fright - ened souls the sure sal - va - tion,
We take it thank - ful - ly and with - out trem - bling,
We shall re - mem - ber all the days we lived through,

and nev - er fails to greet us each new day.
for which, O Lord, you taught us to pre - pare.
out of so good and so be - lov'd a hand.
and our whole life shall then be yours a - lone.

WORDS: Dietrich Bonhoeffer, English version by Fred Pratt Green
MUSIC: C. Hubert H. Parry

INTERCESSOR
11 10.11 10.

84 All Who Love and Serve Your City

1. All who love and serve your cit - y, all who
2. In your day of loss and sor - row, in your
3. In your day of wealth and plen - ty, wast - ed
4. For all days are days of judg - ment, and the
5. Ris - en Lord, shall yet the cit - y be the

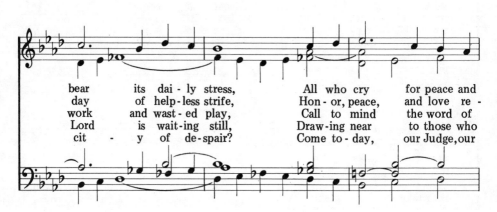

bear its dai - ly stress, All who cry for peace and
day of help - less strife, Hon - or, peace, and love re -
work and wast - ed play, Call to mind the word of
Lord is wait - ing still, Draw - ing near to those who
cit - y of de - spair? Come to - day, our Judge, our

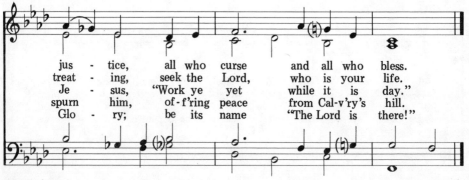

jus - tice, all who curse and all who bless.
treat - ing, seek the Lord, who is your life.
Je - sus, "Work ye yet while it is day."
spurn him, of - f'ring peace from Cal - v'ry's hill.
Glo - ry; be its name "The Lord is there!"

WORDS: Erik Routley
MUSIC: Peter Cutts

BIRABUS
87.87.

1. Break not the cir - cle of en - a - bling love,
2. Come, won - der at this love that comes to life,
3. Come, won - der at the Lord who came and comes,
4. Join then the move - ment of the love that frees,

where peo - ple grow, for - giv - en and for - giv - ing;
where words of free - dom are with hu - mor spo - ken,
to teach the world the craft of hope - ful crav - ing
till peo - ple of what - ev - er race or na - tion,

break not that cir - cle, make it wid - er still,
and peo - ple keep no score of wrong and guilt,
for peace and whole - ness that will fill the earth;
will tru - ly be them - selves, stand on their feet,

till it in - cludes, em - brac - es all the liv - ing.
but will that hu - man bonds re - main un - bro - ken.
he calls his peo - ple to cre - a - tive liv - ing.
see eye to eye with laugh - ter and e - la - tion.

WORDS: Fred Kaan
MUSIC: Doreen Potter

CIRCLE
10 11.10 11

86 God of Gods

Unison

1. God of gods, we sound his prais - es,
2. Chris - tians in their hearts en - throne him,
3. Hail the Christ, the King of glo - ry,
4. Lord, we look for your re - turn - ing,

high - est heav'n its ho - mage brings; earth and all cre -
tell his prais - es wide a - broad; proph - ets, priests, a -
he whose praise the an - gels cry, born to share our
teach us so to walk your ways, hearts and minds your

a - tion rais - es glo - ry to the King of kings.
pos - tles own him, mar - tyrs' crown and saints' re - ward.
hu - man sto - ry, love and la - bor, grieve and die.
will dis - cern - ing, lives a - light with joy and praise.

WORDS: Timothy Dudley-Smith
MUSIC: Christian Strover

GOD OF GODS
87.87.8.8.87.

Ho - ly, ho - ly, ho - ly, name him,
Three in one his glo - ry shar - ing,
By his cross his work com - plet - ed,
In your love and care en - fold us,

Lord of all his hosts pro - claim him, to the e - ver -
earth and heav'n his praise de - clar - ing, praise the high ma -
sin - ners ran - somed, death de - feat - ed, in the glo - ry
by your con - stan - cy up - hold us, may your mer - cy,

last - ing Fa - ther ev - ery tongue in tri - umph sings.
jes - tic Fa - ther, praise the ev - er - last - ing Lord.
of the Fa - ther, Christ as - cend - ed reigns on high.
Lord and Fa - ther, keep us now and all our days.

87 Out of Our Night of Day

1. Out of our night of day— dark - ness at noon,
2. In - to our night of day come with your light,
3. Re - deem our hearts for love, free us from fear;

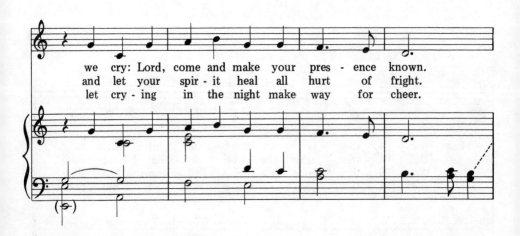

we cry: Lord, come and make your pres - ence known.
and let your spir - it heal all hurt of fright.
let cry - ing in the night make way for cheer.

WORDS: Fred Kaan
MUSIC: Carlton Young

DAYLIGHT
6 4.6 4.

Lord Je - sus, come and help our shak - y faith
Ful - fill our hol - low days that make no sense
Lord, help us keep the prom - ise you have made;

and make us strong to face the pain of
and leave us not in life with - out de -
bring in the day when none shall be a -

life.
fense.
fraid.

88 As the Bridegroom to His Chosen

1. As the bride-groom to his cho - sen, as the king un - to his
2. As the foun - tain in the gar - den, as the can - dle in the
3. As the mu - sic at the ban - quet, as the stamp un - to the
4. As the ru - by in the set - ting, as the hon - ey in the
5. As the sun - shine in the heav - ens, as the im - age in the

realm, As the keep un - to the cas - tle, as the
dark, As the treas - ure in the cof - fer, as the
seal, As the med - i - cine to the faint - ing, as the
comb, As the light with - in the lan - tern, as the
glass, As the fruit up - on the fig tree, as the

pi - lot to the helm, So, Lord, art thou to me.
man - na in the ark, So, Lord, art thou to me.
wine-cup at the meal, So, Lord, art thou to me.
fa - ther in the home, So, Lord, art thou to me.
dew up - on the grass, So, Lord, art thou to me.

WORDS: John Tauler, paraphrased by Emma Frances Bevan
MUSIC: Peter Cutts

BRIDEGROOM
8 7.8 7.6.

Help Us Accept Each Other 89

Unison

1. Help us ac - cept each oth - er as Christ ac - cept - ed us;
2. Teach us, O Lord, your les - sons, as in our dai - ly life
3. Let your ac - cept - ance change us, so that we may be moved
4. Lord, for to - day's en - coun - ters with all who are in need,

teach us as sis - ter, broth - er each per - son to em - brace.
we strug - gle to be hu - man and search for hope and faith.
in liv - ing sit - u - a - tions to do the truth in love;
who hun - ger for ac - cept - ance, for right - eous - ness and bread,

Be pres - ent, Lord, a - mong us and bring us to be - lieve
Teach us to care for peo - ple, for all — not just for some;
to prac - tice your ac - cept - ance un - til we know by heart
we need new eyes for see - ing, new hands for hold - ing on:

we are *our - selves* ac - cept - ed and meant to love and live.
to love them as we find them, or as they may be - come.
the ta - ble of for - give - ness and laugh - ter's heal - ing art.
re - new us with your Spir - it; Lord, free us, make us one!

WORDS: Fred Kaan
MUSIC: John Ness Beck

ACCEPTANCE
7 6.7 6.D.

90 Here, O My Lord

1. Here O my Lord, I
2. I have no help but

see thee face to face; Here would I
thine, nor do I need An - oth - er

touch and han - dle things un - seen,
arm but thine to lean up - on.

WORDS: Horatius Bonar
MUSIC: M. Lee Suitor

FACE TO FACE
LM

Here grasp with firm - er hand e - ter - nal grace,
It is e - nough, my Lord, e - nough in - deed;

And all my wea - ri -
My strength is in thy

repeat, *ad lib.*

ness up - on thee lean.
might, thy might a - lone.
A - men.

91 God Is Here!

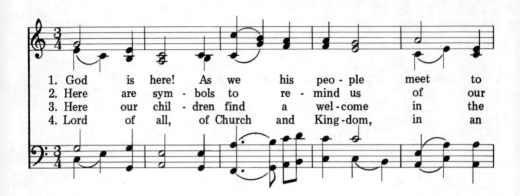

1. God is here! As we his peo - ple meet to
2. Here are sym - bols to re - mind us of our
3. Here our chil - dren find a wel - come in the
4. Lord of all, of Church and King - dom, in an

of - fer praise and prayer, May we find in
life - long need of grace; Here are ta - ble,
Shep - herd's flock and fold, Here, as bread and
age of change and doubt Keep us faith - ful

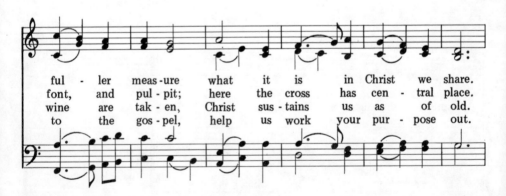

ful - ler meas - ure what it is in Christ we share.
font, and pul - pit; here the cross has cen - tral place.
wine are tak - en, Christ sus - tains us as of old.
to the gos - pel, help us work your pur - pose out.

WORDS: Fred Pratt Green
MUSIC: Cyril V. Taylor

ABBOT'S LEIGH
8 7.8 7.D.

Here, as in the world a - round us, all our
Here in hon - es - ty of preach - ing, here in
Here the ser - vants of the Ser - vant seek in
Here, in this day's ded - i - ca - tion, all we

var - ied skills and arts Wait the com - ing
si - lence, as in speech, Here, in new - ness
wor - ship to ex - plore What it means in
have to give, re - ceive: We, who can - not

of the Spir - it in - to o - pen minds and hearts.
and re - new - al, God the Spir - it comes to each.
dai - ly liv - ing to be - lieve and to a - dore.
live with - out you, we a - dore you! we be - lieve!

92 O God of Every Nation

Unison

1. O God of ev-ery na - tion, of ev-ery race and land,
2. From search for wealth and pow - er and scorn of truth and right,
3. Lord, strength-en all who la - bor that all may find re - lease
4. Keep bright in us the vi - sion of days when war shall cease,

Re - deem your whole cre - a - tion with your al - might-y hand;
From trust in bombs that show - er de - struc-tion through the night,
From fear of rat - tling sa - ber, from dread of war's in - crease;
When ha - tred and di - vi - sion give way to love and peace,

Where hate and fear di - vide us and bit - ter threats are hurled,
From pride of race and sta - tion and blind-ness to your way,
When hope and cour-age fal - ter, Lord, let your voice be heard;
Till dawns the morn-ing glo - rious when truth and jus - tice reign,

In love and mer - cy guide us and heal our strife - torn world.
De - liv - er ev - ery na - tion, e - ter - nal God, we pray.
With faith that none can al - ter, your ser - vants un - der - gird.
And Christ shall rule vic - to - rious o'er all the world's do - main.

WORDS: William W. Reid, Jr.
MUSIC: Dale Wood

TUOLUMNE
7 6.7 6.D.

1. O Christ the Lord, O Christ the King, who wide the gates of death didst fling, Whose place up-on Cre-a-tion's throne by Eas-ter tri-umph was made known, Rule now on earth from realms a-bove, sub-due the na-tions by thy love.

2. Lord, vin-di-cate a-gainst our greed the weak, whose tears thy jus-tice plead; Thy pit-y, Lord, on all who lie bro-ken by war and tyr-an-ny; Show them the cross which thou didst bear, give them the power that con-quered there.

3. Let those whose pride u-surps thy throne ac-know-ledge thou art Lord a-lone; Cause those whose lust tor-ments man-kind thy wrath to know, thy mer-cy find; Make all the reb-el world pro-claim the might-y power of thy blest name.

4. So shall cre-a-tion's bond-age cease, its pangs of woe give birth to peace; And all the earth, re-deemed by thee, shall know a glo-rious li-ber-ty: O haste the time, make short the days, till all our cries dis-solve in praise.

WORDS: R. T. Brooks
MUSIC: Arthur S. Warrell

FARMBOROUGH
88.88.88.

94 If You Have Ears

Unison

1. If you have ears then lis - ten to what the Spir - it says, and
3. If you have buds, for tast - ing the ap - ple of God's eye, then
5. If you can smell the per - fume of life, the feast of earth, then

1. give an o - pen hear - ing to won - der and sur - prise.
3. go, en - joy cre - a - tion and peo - ple on the way.
5. sow the seeds of laugh - ter and tend the shoots of mirth.

2. If you have eyes for hear - ing the word in hu - man form, then
4. If you have hands for car - ing, then pray that you may know the
6. Come, peo - ple, to your sen - ses and cel - e - brate the day! For

Vs. 2,4   Vs. 6

2. let your love be tell - ing and your com - pass - ion warm.
4. ten - der art of lov - ing our world of touch and go.
6. God gives wine for wa - ter, the gift of light for grey.

WORDS: Fred Kaan
MUSIC: Alec Wyton

LISTEN
76.76.D.

For the Fruit of All Creation 95

Unison

1. For the fruit of all cre-a-tion, thanks be to God.
2. In the just re-ward of la-bor, God's will is done.
3. For the har-vests of the Spir-it, thanks be to God.

For his gifts to ev-ery na-tion, thanks be to God.
In the help we give our neigh-bor, God's will is done.
For the good we all in-her-it, thanks be to God.

For the plow-ing, sow-ing, reap-ing, si-lent growth while we are sleep-ing,
In our world-wide task of car-ing for the hun-gry and de-spair-ing,
For the won-ders that as-tound us, for the truths that still con-found us,

Fu-ture needs in earth's safe-keep-ing, thanks be to God.
In the har-vests we are shar-ing, God's will is done.
Most of all, that love has found us, thanks be to God.

WORDS: Fred Pratt Green
MUSIC: Emma Lou Diemer

SANTA BARBARA
8 4.8 4.8 8.8 4.

96 Sometimes a Light Surprises

Unison

1. Some-times a light sur - pris - es the Child of God who
2. In ho - ly con - tem - pla - tion we sweet - ly then pur -
3. It can bring with it noth - ing but he will bear us
4. Though vine nor fig tree nei - ther their wont - ed fruit should

sings; It is the Lord, who ris - es with
sue The theme of God's sal - va - tion, and
through; Who gives the lil - ies cloth - ing will
bear, Though all the field should with - er, nor

heal - ing in his wings. When com - forts are de -
find it ev - er new; Set free from pres - ent
clothe his peo - ple, too; Be - neath the spread - ing
flocks nor herds be there; Yet, God the same a -

WORDS: William Cowper
MUSIC: Jane Marshall

SURPRISE
7 6.7 6.D.

clin - ing, he grants the soul a - gain A
sor - row, we cheer - ful - ly can say, Let
heav - ens no crea - ture but is fed; And
bid - ing, his praise shall tune my voice; For,

sea - son of clear shin - ing, to cheer it af - ter
the un-known to - mor - row bring with it what it
he who feeds the ra - vens will give his chil - dren
while in him con - fid - ing, I can - not but re -

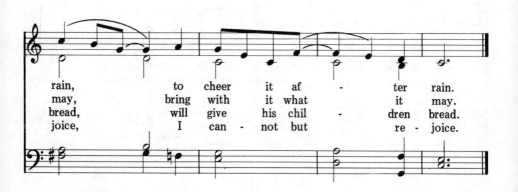

rain, to cheer it af - ter rain.
may, bring with it what it may.
bread, will give his chil - dren bread.
joice, I can - not but re - joice.

97 There's a Quiet Understanding

1. There's a qui - et un - der - stand - ing
2. And we know when we're to - geth - er,

when we're gath - ered in the Spir - it, It's a prom - ise
shar - ing love and un - der - stand - ing, That our broth - ers

that he gives us, when we gath - er in his name.
and our sis - ters feel the one - ness that he brings.

WORDS and MUSIC: Tedd Smith

QUIET UNDERSTANDING
Irregular

There's a love we feel in Je - sus, there's a man - na
Thank you, thank you, thank you, Je - sus, for the way you

that he feeds us, It's a prom - ise that he gives us
love and feed us, For the man - y ways you lead us,

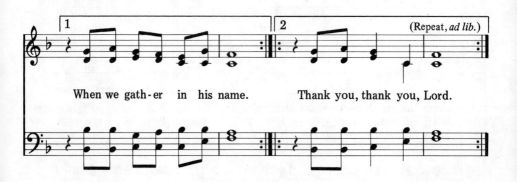

1 When we gath - er in his name. **2** (Repeat, *ad lib.*) Thank you, thank you, Lord.

98 Open, Lord, My Inward Ear

Moderate, ♩ = 66

1. O - pen, Lord, my in - ward ear and bid my heart re -
2. Show me, as my soul can bear, the depth of in - bred
3. Lord, my time is in thy hand, my soul to thee con -

joice; Bid my qui - et spir - it hear thy com - fort -
sin; All my un - be - lief de - clare, the pride that
vert; Thou canst make me un - der - stand, though I am

a - ble voice; Nev - er in the whirl - wind found, or
lurks with - in: Take me, whom thy - self hast bought, and
slow of heart; Thine in whom I live and move, thine,

where the earth - quake rocks the place; Still and si - lent
bring in - to cap - tiv - i - ty Ev - ery high as -
Lord, the work, the praise is thine! Thou art wis - dom,

WORDS: Charles Wesley
MUSIC: Malcolm Williamson

OBEDIENCE
76.76.78.75.

Mercy, Blessing, Favor, Grace 99

Unison

1. Mer - cy, bless - ing, fa - vor, grace,
2. Shout in tri - umph, sing in praise!
3. Har - vests year by year pro - claim

sav - ing pow'r to us be shown; bright - ness of the
Peo - ples all, pro - claim his worth. Just and right - eous
bless - ings new in plen - ty poured; all the earth shall

Fa - ther's face to the na - tions now be known.
are his ways, sov - 'reign Lord of all the earth.
fear his Name, all his peo - ple praise the Lord.

WORDS: Timothy Dudley-Smith
MUSIC: David G. Wilson

MONKSGATE
7.7.7.7.

100 Lord, Let Me Love

Unison

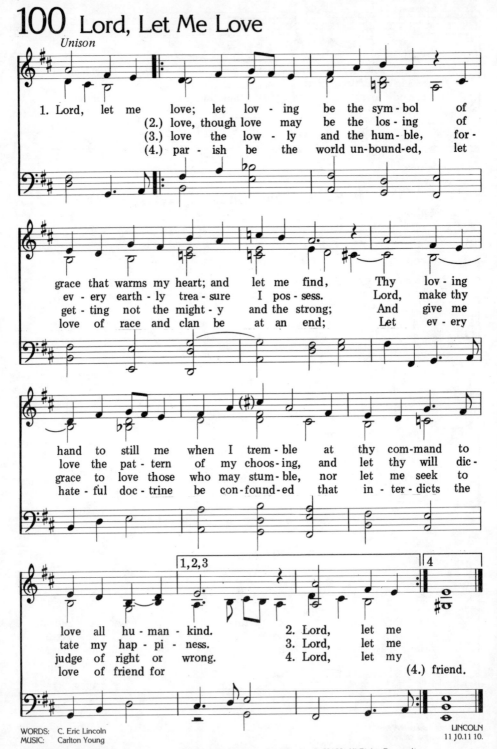

1. Lord, let me love; let lov-ing be the sym-bol of
(2.) love, though love may be the los-ing of
(3.) love the low-ly and the hum-ble, for-let
(4.) par-ish be the world un-bound-ed, let

grace that warms my heart; and let me find, Thy lov-ing
ev-ery earth-ly trea-sure I pos-sess. Lord, make thy
get-ting not the might-y and the strong; And give me
love of race and clan be at an end; Let ev-ery

hand to still me when I trem-ble at thy com-mand to
love the pat-tern of my choos-ing, and let thy will dic-
grace to love those who may stum-ble, nor let me seek to
hate-ful doc-trine be con-found-ed that in-ter-dicts the

1, 2, 3
love all hu-man-kind.
tate my hap-pi-ness.
judge of right or wrong.
love of friend for

4
2. Lord, let me
3. Lord, let me
4. Lord, let my
(4.) friend.

WORDS: C. Eric Lincoln
MUSIC: Carlton Young

LINCOLN
11 10.11 10.

I Wonder Why? 101

Unison

I won-der why, I won-der why?

1. If his dis - ci - ples were like us here Why they all
2. If they were peo - ple like you and me Why they re -
3. If they were sol - diers like boys we know Why they all
4. If they were lead - ers like those we trust Why they were
5. They did not know him and love him then? Would we al -

left him and ran in fear, As the world did cru-ci-fy,
fused then to set him free, For the crowd yelled: "Cru-ci-fy,
beat him and mocked him so, Then went out to cru-ci-fy,
cru - el and so un - just When they judged to cru-ci-fy,
low him to die a - gain? Would the world still cru-ci-fy,

cru-ci-fy him? Oh, I won-der why?
cru-ci-fy him!" Oh, I won-der why?
cru-ci-fy him? Oh, I won-der why?
cru-ci-fy him? Oh, I won-der why? (last time)
cru-ci-fy him? Oh, I won-der why? I won-der why?

WORDS and MUSIC: Richard Avery and Donald Marsh

WILCOX
Irregular

102 We Plow and Sow with Tractors

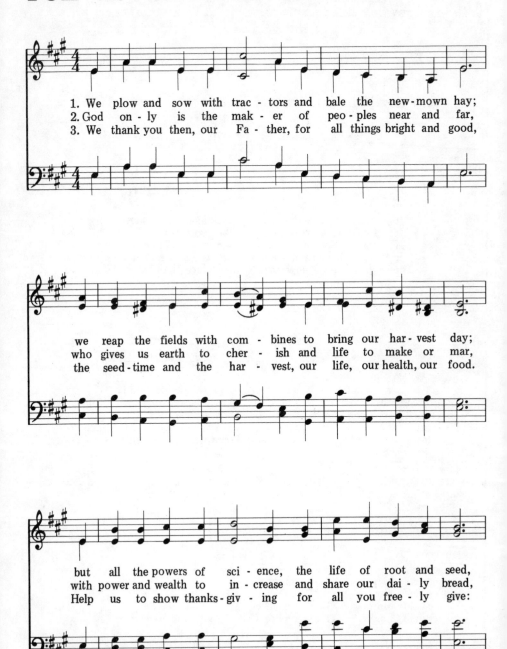

1. We plow and sow with trac - tors and bale the new-mown hay;
2. God on - ly is the mak - er of peo - ples near and far,
3. We thank you then, our Fa - ther, for all things bright and good,

we reap the fields with com - bines to bring our har - vest day;
who gives us earth to cher - ish and life to make or mar,
the seed - time and the har - vest, our life, our health, our food.

but all the powers of sci - ence, the life of root and seed,
with power and wealth to in - crease and share our dai - ly bread,
Help us to show thanks - giv - ing for all you free - ly give:

WORDS: Brian Wren
MUSIC: Johann A. P. Schulz

WIR PFLÜGEN
7 6.7 6.D. Ref.

the air and earth and wa - ter are gifts to meet our need.
that friends might wel - come strang - ers and ev - ery child be fed.
to love you in our neigh - bor, and by the way we live.

Refrain

See God's gifts with - in us, a - round us, and a - bove?

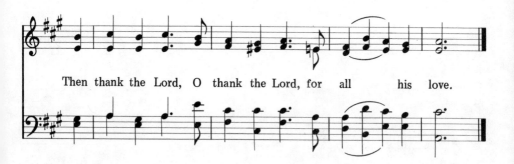

Then thank the Lord, O thank the Lord, for all his love.

103 Praise God from Whom All Blessings Flow

Praise God from whom all bless-ings flow, Praise Him, all crea-tures here be-low. Praise Him a-bove, ye heav'n-ly host; praise Fa-ther, Son and Ho-ly Ghost. A-men. A-men. A-men. A-men. A-men. A-men. A-men. A-men. A-men. A-men.

WORDS: Thomas Ken
MUSIC: Richard Avery and Donald Marsh

PORT JERVIS
L M Amens

All That Christians Have in Life 104

1. All that Chris-tians have in life is a sto - ry and a song,
2. All that Chris-tians are in life: they are peo - ple of "the way,"
3. All that Chris-tians have and are is a pic-ture of their Lord,

bread and wine, a lit - tle faith and a long-ing to be - long;
led by hunch - es, lured by hope, now ex - cit - ed, then a - fraid;
is a sig - nal and a glimpse, is a ges - ture and a word;

that is all they have. That is all they have.
that is what they are. That is what they are.
that is where they are. That is where they are.

WORDS: Fred Kaan
MUSIC: Carlton Young

CREDO
77.77.55.

105 Lord, Whose Love in Humble Service

1. Lord, whose love in hum - ble ser - vice bore the
2. Still your chil - dren wan - der home-less; still the
3. As we wor - ship, grant us vi - sion, till your
4. Called from wor - ship in - to ser - vice, forth in

weight of hu - man need, Who up - on the
hun - gry cry for bread; Still the cap - tives
love's re - veal - ing light In its height and
your dear name we go, To the child, the

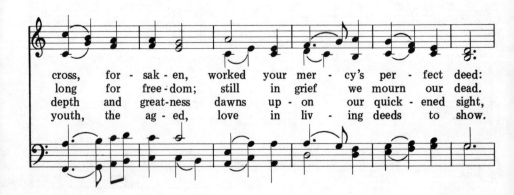

cross, for - sak - en, worked your mer - cy's per - fect deed:
long for free-dom; still in grief we mourn our dead.
depth and great-ness dawns up - on our quick - ened sight,
youth, the ag - ed, love in liv - ing deeds to show.

WORDS: Albert F. Bayly
MUSIC: Cyril V. Taylor

ABBOT'S LEIGH
87.87.D.

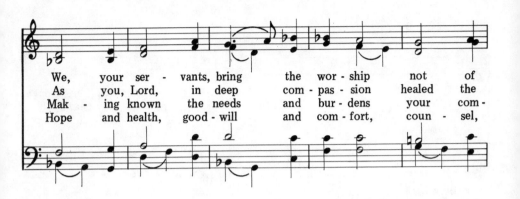

We, your ser - vants, bring the wor - ship not of
As you, Lord, in deep com - pas - sion healed the
Mak - ing known the needs and bur - dens your com -
Hope and health, good - will and com - fort, coun - sel,

voice a - lone, but heart; Con - se - cra - ting
sick and freed the soul, Use the love your
pas - sion bids us bear, Stir - ring us to
aid and peace we give, That your chil - dren,

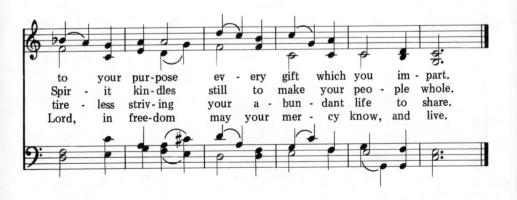

to your pur - pose ev - ery gift which you im - part.
Spir - it kin - dles still to make your peo - ple whole.
tire - less striv - ing your a - bun - dant life to share.
Lord, in free - dom may your mer - cy know, and live.

106 O Jesus Christ, Our Lord Most Dear

1. O Je - sus Christ, our
2. As in thy heav'n - ly
3. And all this life, let

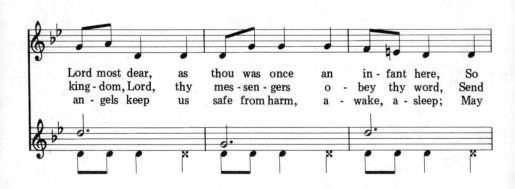

Lord most dear, as thou was once an in - fant here, So
king - dom, Lord, thy mes - sen - gers o - bey thy word, Send
an - gels keep us safe from harm, a - wake, a - sleep; May

give this child of thine, we pray, thy grace and bless - ing
forth the suc - cor of thy might to shield this child both
we not bear the cross in vain, but with thy saints a

WORDS: Henrich von Laufenburg, trans. by Catherine Winkworth
MUSIC: Richard Dirksen

ANGUS
L M Ref.

107 My Dear Redeemer

♩ = 100

1. My dear Re - deem - er and my Lord, I read my
2. Such was thy truth and such thy zeal, such def - erence
3. Cold moun-tains and the mid - night air wit-nessed the
4. Be thou my pat - tern, make me bear more of thy

du - ty in thy Word; But in my life the law ap -
to thy Fa-ther's will, Such love, and meek - ness so di -
fer - vor of thy prayer; The des - ert thy temp - ta - tions
gra - cious im - age here; Then God, the Judge, shall own my

pears drawn out in liv - ing char - ac - ters. I read my
vine, I would tran - scribe and make them mine. I read my
knew, thy con - flict and thy vic - tory too. I read my
name a - mongst the fol - lowers of the Lamb. I read my

pp

du - ty in thy Word, My dear Re - deem - er and my Lord.

WORDS: Isaac Watts
MUSIC: Malcolm Williamson

LIFE OF CHRIST
LM Ref.

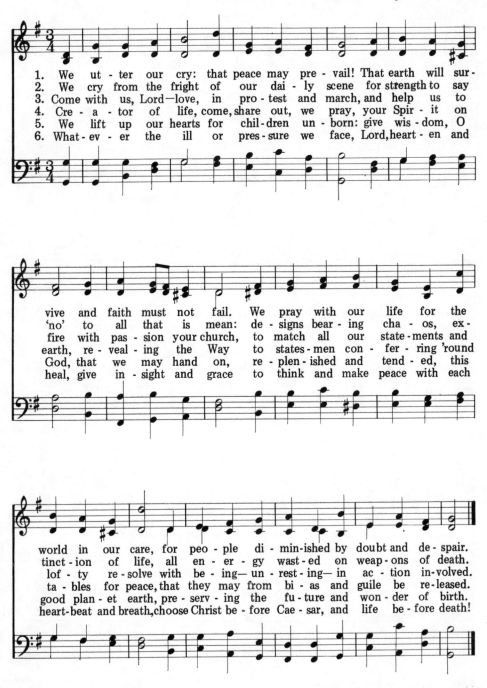

1. We ut-ter our cry: that peace may pre-vail! That earth will sur-vive and faith must not fail. We pray with our life for the world in our care, for peo-ple di-min-ished by doubt and de-spair.

2. We cry from the fright of our dai-ly scene for strength to say 'no' to all that is mean: de-signs bear-ing cha-os, ex-tinct-ion of life, all en-er-gy wast-ed on weap-ons of death.

3. Come with us, Lord—love, in pro-test and march, and help us to fire with pas-sion your church, to match all our state-ments and lof-ty re-solve with be-ing— un-rest-ing— in ac-tion in-volved.

4. Cre-a-tor of life, come, share out, we pray, your Spir-it on earth, re-veal-ing the Way to states-men con-fer-ring 'round ta-bles for peace, that they may from bi-as and guile be re-leased.

5. We lift up our hearts for chil-dren un-born: give wis-dom, O God, that we may hand on, re-plen-ished and tend-ed, this good plan-et earth, pre-serv-ing the fu-ture and won-der of birth.

6. What-ev-er the ill or pres-sure we face, Lord, heart-en and heal, give in-sight and grace to think and make peace with each heart-beat and breath, choose Christ be-fore Cae-sar, and life be-fore death!

WORDS: Fred Kaan
MUSIC: attr. William Croft

HANOVER
10 10.11 11.

109 Lord, for the Years

Unison

1. Lord, for the years your love has kept and guid - ed,
2. Lord, for that Word, the Word of life which fires us,
3. Lord, for our land, in this our gen - er - a - tion,
4. Lord, for our world, when we dis - own and doubt him,
5. Lord, for our - selves; in liv - ing power re - make us —

urged and in - spired us, cheered us on our way;
speaks to our hearts and sets our souls a - blaze;
spir - its op - pressed by plea - sure, wealth and care;
love - less in strength, and com - fort - less in pain;
self on the cross and Christ up - on the throne—

sought us and saved us, par - doned and pro - vid - ed,
teach - es and trains, re - bukes us and in - spires us,
for young and old, for com - mon - wealth and na - tion,
hun - gry and help - less, lost in - deed with - out him,
past put be - hind us, for the fu - ture take us,

WORDS: Timothy Dudley-Smith
MUSIC: Michael Baughen and David Wilson

LORD OF THE YEARS
11 10.11 10.

Lord of the years, we bring our thanks to-day.
Lord of the Word, re-ceive your peo-ple's praise.
Lord of our land, be pleased to hear our prayer.
Lord of the world, we pray that Christ may reign.
Lord of our lives, to live for Christ a-lone.

Become to Us the Living Bread 110

1. Be-come to us the liv-ing bread by which the Chris-tian
2. Be-come the nev-er-fail-ing wine, the spring of joy that
3. May Chris-tians all with one ac-cord u-nite a-round the

life is fed, re-newed, and great-ly com-fort-ed,
shall in-cline our hearts to bear the cov-enant sign,
sa-cred board to praise your ho-ly name, O Lord,

Al - le - lu - ia, al - le - lu - ia!

WORDS: Miriam Drury
MUSIC: Jane Marshall

ONE ACCORD
LM ALLELUIAS

111 We Have Heard It, We Have Seen It

1. We have heard it, we have seen it, We have
2. On - ly one who loves an - oth - er Walks from

touched it with our hands, And this love of Christ our
dark - ness in - to light, Loves "the least of these, God's

Sav - ior Far ex - ceeds His laws' de - mands. Thus we
child - ren," Though re - ject - ed in our sight. When we

WORDS: Harriet Ziegenhals, based on 1 John 1:1-4
MUSIC: Harriet Ziegenhals

ILSE
87.87.9.88.

know that God is with us, And in Him is no
heal the bro - ken heart - ed, Give un - spar - ing what -

dark-ness at all, That our sins have been for -
ev - er the call, We ful - fill Christ's new com -

giv - en To com - plete the joy of us all!
mand - ment To com - plete the joy of us all!

112 My Shepherd Is the Lord

ANTIPHON I

My shep-herd is the Lord, noth-ing in-deed shall I want.

ANTIPHON II

His good-ness shall fol-low me al-ways to the end of my days.

PSALM

1.
2.   The Lord is my   shepherd;   there is
3.   He   guides me a - long the right path;   he is
4. You have pre -   pared   a   banquet for   me   in the
5.   Surely   goodness and kindness shall follow me   all the
6.   To the   Father   and Son give   glory,   give

WORDS: Psalm 22(23), Grail Version
MUSIC: Music and Antiphon I by Joseph Gelineau
         Antiphon II by A. Gregory Murray

GELINEAU
Irregular

Psalm 22(23) from THE PSALMS: A NEW TRANSLATION by permission of the Grail, England.
Music and Antiphon I Copyright Ed. Le Cerf, Paris 1953.
Antiphon II used by permission of the Grail, England.

113 The Grace of Life Is Theirs

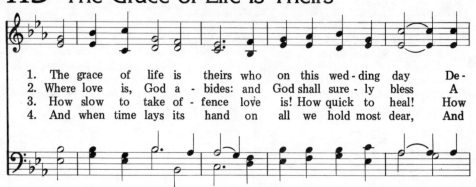

1. The grace of life is theirs who on this wed-ding day   De-
2. Where love is, God a-bides: and God shall sure-ly bless   A
3. How slow to take of-fence love is! How quick to heal!   How
4. And when time lays its hand on all we hold most dear,   And

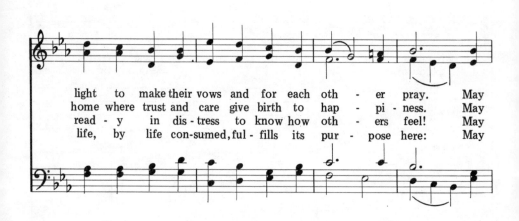

light to make their vows and for each oth-er pray.   May
home where trust and care give birth to hap-pi-ness.   May
read-y in dis-tress to know how oth-ers feel!   May
life, by life con-sumed, ful-fills its pur-pose here: May

they, O Lord, to-geth-er prove the last-ing joy of Chris-tian love.
they, O Lord, to-geth-er prove the last-ing joy of such a love.
they, O Lord, to-geth-er prove the last-ing joy of such a love.
we, O Lord, to-geth-er prove the last-ing joy of Chris-tian love.

WORDS: Fred Pratt Green
MUSIC: John Ireland

LOVE UNKNOWN
12 12.8 8.

That Boy-Child of Mary 114

Refrain
Unison

That boy-child of Ma — ry was born in a sta — ble, A

Fine

man-ger his cra — dle in Beth — le - hem.

1. What shall we call him, child of the man — ger?
2. His name is Je — su, God ev - er with us,
3. How can he save us, how can he help us,
4. Gift of the Fa — ther, to hu - man moth - er,
5. One with the Fa — ther, he is our Sav - ior,
6. Glad - ly we praise him, love and a - dore him,

D. C. al Fine

What name is giv - en in Beth - le - hem?
God giv - en for us, in Beth - le - hem.
Born here a - mong us, in Beth - le - hem?
Makes him our broth - er of Beth - le - hem.
Heav - en sent Help - er of Beth - le - hem.
Give our - selves to him, of Beth - le - hem.

WORDS: Tom Colvin
MUSIC: Traditional Malawi Melody, adapted by Tom Colvin

BLANTYRE
Irregular

115 How Can We Name a Love

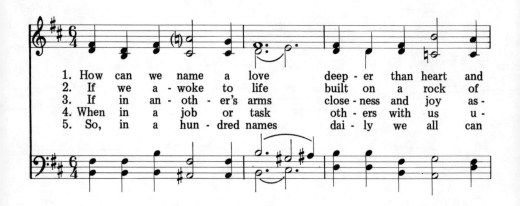

1. How can we name a love   deep - er than heart and
2. If   we a - woke to life   built on a rock of
3. If   in an - oth - er's arms close - ness and joy as -
4. When in a   job or task   oth - ers with us   u -
5. So, in a hun - dred names dai - ly we   all   can

mind,   ba - sic to all we know or think or
care   that asked no great re - ward but firm, as -
tound,   and as we take and give we die and
nite,   work - ing at some - thing new to make or
meet   sig - nals of love un - known at work, at

WORDS: Brian Wren
MUSIC: Malcolm Williamson

MERCER STREET
SMD

do or seek or find? 'Look at your life, your world:
sured, was sim - ply there, we can, with par - ents' names,
live, are lost and found, or if by oth - ers' trust
do with shared de - light, think how our Part - ner's aims
home or in the street. Yet on these terms a - lone

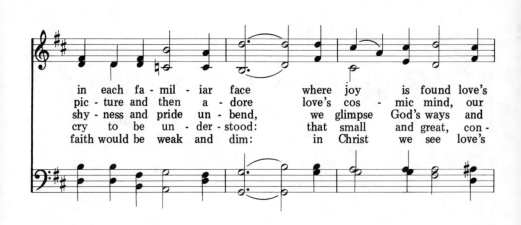

in each fa - mil - iar face where joy is found love's
pic - ture and then a - dore love's cos - mic mind, our
shy - ness and pride un - bend, we glimpse God's ways and
cry to be un - der - stood: that small and great, con -
faith would be weak and dim: in Christ we see love's

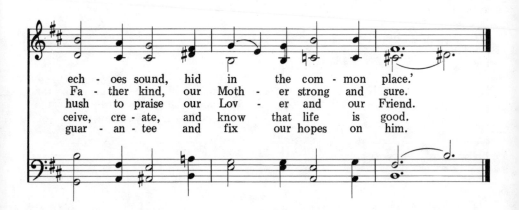

ech - oes sound, hid in the com - mon place.'
Fa - ther kind, our Moth - er strong and sure.
hush to praise our Lov - er and our Friend.
ceive, cre - ate, and know that life is good.
guar - an - tee and fix our hopes on him.

116 God Is! Rejoice!

WORDS AND MUSIC: Richard Avery and Donald Marsh

ROWAND
Irregular

bill - ions of stars, In the earth, in the si - lent
clut - ter, the crime, And our lost hon - es - ty and
long rest - less nights, Full of doubt, fran - tic and a -

sea; God is known in the hands with the ug - ly
shame, There's God's jus - tice, there's peace, and with work and
lone, We shall rise from des - pair to ex - al - ted

D.C.

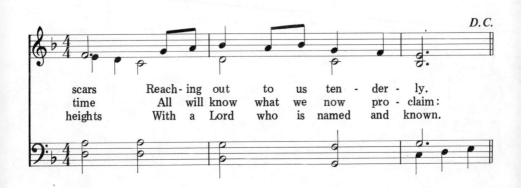

scars Reach - ing out to us ten - der - ly.
time All will know what we now pro - claim:
heights With a Lord who is named and known.

117 Divided Our Pathways

Refrain

♩ = 69

Di - vid - ed our path-ways, and heav - y our guilt; bur-den'd, un - see - ing, we grope for the one way. Far from our home, O Fa - ther, we call out 'Heal us, for-

WORDS: Christopher Coelho, O.F.M.
MUSIC: Christopher Coelho, O.F.M., arr. by Erik Routley

PATHWAYS
Irregular

Fine

give us: bring us to-geth-er in Je-sus your Son!'

Cantor

1,2,3

1. Holy Father, keep those you have giv-en me true to your Name, so__ that
2. Father, may they be one in us as you are in me and I am in you, so that the
3. I have given them the glo-ry that you gave to me, that__
4. With me in them and you in me may they be so com-plete-ly u-nited, (to Vs.4)

D. C. 4

they may_____ all be one as we are one.
world may come to be-lieve it was you who sent__ me.
they may_____ all be one as we are one.

(4.) that the world may know

D. C. al Fine

that it was you who sent me, and that you love them as much as you love me.

118 O Paradise

Slow and flowing
Unison

1. O Par-a-dise, O Par-a-dise, who does not crave for rest?
2. O Par-a-dise, O Par-a-dise, the world is grow-ing old;
3. O Par-a-dise, O Par-a-dise, we long to sin no more;
4. O Par-a-dise, O Par-a-dise, we shall not wait for long;
5. Lord Je-sus, King of Par-a-dise, O keep us in thy love,

Who would not seek the hap-py land where they that loved are blest:
Who would not be at rest and free where love is nev-er cold?
We long to be as pure on earth as on thy spot-less shore:
E'en now the lov-ing ear may catch faint frag-ments of thy song:
And guide us to that hap-py land of per-fect rest a-bove:

Refrain-*Four parts*

Where loy-al hearts and true stand ev-er in the light, All rap-ture thro' and

thro' in God's most ho-ly sight. O Par-a-dise, O Par-a-dise!

WORDS: Frederick W. Faber
MUSIC: Malcolm Williamson

PARADISE
CM Ref.

God Has Set Us Free 119

Unison

1. God has set us free for free-dom, for re-
2. Ties of kin-dred are our bond-age: we the
3. God un-ties our hands for lov-ing, man or
4. Hu-man hearts re-main in tur-moil till they
5. Give us free-dom, Lord, to serve you, show us

spond-ing 'yes' or 'no.' Free-dom is his gift and
mem-bers, he the head. God has made us in his
wom-an, chil-dren, friends, car-ing for the oth-er's
find their rest in God. He is source of peace and
where we ought to go, nev-er rest-ing till all

Refrain
(Four parts)

call-ing, he has let his peo-ple go.
im-age; love has made us free in-deed.
whole-ness; love is kind and un-der-stands. Free-dom is to
free-dom, gives us Christ in flesh and blood.
peo-ple's cups are full and o-ver-flow.

peo-ple what air is to the birds. Free-dom is be-

long-ing, break-ing bread, shar-ing words.

WORDS: Fred Kaan
MUSIC: Doreen Potter

EMANCIPATION
8 7.8 7. Ref.

120 A Song Was Heard at Christmas

1. A song was heard at Christ - mas to wake the
2. A star was seen at Christ - mas, a her - ald
3. A tree was grown at Christ - mas, a sap - ling
4. A child was born at Christ - mas when Christ - mas

mid - night sky; a Sav - ior's birth, and peace on
and a sign, that all might know the way to
green and young; no tin - sel bright with can - dle
first be - gan; the Lord of all a ba - by

earth, and praise to God on high. The an - gels sang at
go to find the child di - vine. The wise men watched at
light up - on its branch - es hung. But He who came at
small, the Son of God made man. For love is ours at

Christ - mas with all the hosts a - bove, and still we
Christ - mas in some far east - ern land, and still the
Christ - mas our sins and sor - rows bore, and still we
Christ - mas, and life and light re - stored, and so we

WORDS: Timothy Dudley-Smith
MUSIC: John B. Dykes

ALFORD
7 6.8 6.D.

See, to Us a Child Is Born 121

sing the new - born King, his glo - ry and his love.
wise in star - ry skies dis - cern their Mak - er's hand.
name his tree of shame our life for - ev - er - more.
praise through end - less days the Sav - ior, Christ the Lord.

Choir   *Congregation*

1. See, to us a child is born— Glo - ry
2. On his shoul - der rule shall rest— In him
3. Might - y God, who mer - cy brings— Lord of
4. Ev - er - last - ing Prince of Peace— Truth and

Choir

breaks on Christ - mas morn! Now to us a Son is
all the earth be blest! Wise and won - der - ful his
lords and King of kings! Fa - ther of e - ter - nal
right - eous - ness in - crease! He shall reign from shore to

Congregation

giv'n— Praise to God in high - est heav'n!
Name— Heav - en's Lord in hu - man frame!
days— Ev - ery crea - ture sing his praise!
shore— Christ is King for ev - er - more!

WORDS: Timothy Dudley-Smith
MUSIC: W. H. Monk, *The Parish Choir,* 1850

INNOCENTS
7 7.7 7.

122 Of All the Spirit's Gifts to Me

1. Of all the Spir - it's gifts to me,
2. He shows me love is at the root
3. He shows me that if I pos - sess
4. Though what's a - head is mys - ter - y,
5. We go in peace— but made a - ware

I pray that I may nev - er cease To take and
Of ev - ery gift sent from a - bove, Of ev - ery
A love no e - vil can de - stroy, How ev - er
And life it - self is ours on lease, Each day the
That in a need - y world like this Our clear - est

trea - sure most these three: Love, joy, and peace.
flower, of ev - ery fruit, That God is love.
great is my dis - tress, That this is joy.
Spir - it says to me: Go forth in peace.
pur - pose is to share Love, joy, and peace.

WORDS: Fred Pratt Green
MUSIC: Norman Cocker

RIPPONDEN
888.4.

Now Join We, to Praise the Creator 123

Unison

1. Now join we, to praise the cre - a - tor, our voi - ces in
2. We thank you, O God, for your good - ness, for the joy and a -
3. But al - so of need and star - va - tion we sing with con -
4. We cry for the plight of the hun - gry while har - vests are
5. The song grows in depth and in wide - ness: the earth and its
6. Then teach us, O Lord of the har - vest, to be hum - ble in

wor - ship and song; we stand to re - call with thanks -
bun - dance of crops, for food that is stored in our
cern and de - spair— of skills that we used for de -
left on the field, for or - chards ne - glect - ed and
peo - ple are one. There can be no thanks with - out
all that we claim; to share what we have with the

giv - ing that to him all sea - sons be - long.
cup - boards, for all we can buy in our shops.
struct - ion, of land that is burnt and laid bare.
wast - ing, for pro - duce from mar - kets with - held.
giv - ing, no words with - out deeds that are done.
na - tions, to care for the world in your name.

WORDS: Fred Kaan
MUSIC: Geoffrey Laycock

HARVEST
98.98.

124 In Bethlehem of Judah

Unison (or Two parts)

1. In Beth - le - hem of Ju - dah, a - mong the ver - y poor - est, a child was born of Ma - ry, of all God's gifts the rich - est.
2. The work - ers from the fields came, to greet the King of heav - en; the clev - er, rich and might - y knew noth - ing of his birth then.
3. He came to bring a new way of liv - ing with each oth - er by shar - ing and by lov - ing and serv - ing one an - oth - er.
4. The hun - gry, poor or sin - ful. Or those whose lives are bro - ken can find in him their free - dom and glo - ry as God's chil - dren.
5. So wel - come to the morn - ing of bless - ed Je - su's birth - day. Let's give our - selves to Je - su and live for - ev - er his way.

Poor folk hear him glad - ly, yours will be the King - dom.
Rich folk share your for - tunes, Je - su bids you wel - come.

[1] [2]

WORDS: Tom Colvin, inspired by a Traditional Tumbuka Hymn by Jessie Nyagondwe
MUSIC: Traditional Northern Malawi Melody

TAMKWIMBA KWA JESU
77.77. Ref.

God Is Hope and God Is Now! 125

Unison

1. God is hope, and God is now! Hope, de-spite dis-tress and dark-ness,
2. God is hope, and God is now! Hope not on-ly for to-mor-row—
3. God is hope, and God is now! Hope for earth, and hope for heav-en,

war and fam-ine, woe and fear; hope though hearts are sick with sor-row,
death de-feat-ed, heav-en won— but for pres-ent needs and grac-es,
hope not meant for us a-lone; then to all God's hu-man chil-dren

hope a-far, yet rich-ly near: heart, a-rise! your faith a-vow,
ours to-day through Christ the Son. Spir-it-wrought, we know not how,
we must make his Gos-pel known. Up, my soul, make good your vow—

God is hope, and God is now, God is hope, and God is now!
God is hope, and God is now, God is hope, and God is now!
take God's hope, and share it now! Take God's hope, and share it now!

WORDS: Margaret Clarkson
MUSIC: Donald P. Hustad

BROADFIELDS
7 8.7 8.7 7.7 7.

126 We Are Your People

Descant, Vs. 6 only

6. Lord, in dif - f'rent ways,

Unison

1. We are your peo - ple— Lord, by your grace,
2. How can we dem - on-strate your love and care—
3. Called to por - tray you, help us to live
4. Glad of tra - di - tion, help us to see
5. Joined in com - mun - i - ty, break - ing your bread,
6. Lord, as we min - is - ter in dif - f'rent ways,

may all we're do - ing show that you're liv - ing, meet - ing your

you dare to make us Christ to our neigh - bors of ev - ery
speak - ing or list'n - ing? Bat - tling or serv - ing? Help us to
clos - er than neigh - bors, o - pen to stran - gers, a - ble to
in all life's chang - ing where you are lead - ing, where our best
may we dis - cov - er gifts in each oth - er, will - ing to
may all we're do - ing show that you're liv - ing, meet - ing your

WORDS: Brian Wren
MUSIC: John Wilson

WHITFIELD
Irregular

Christ Is the World's Light 127

Vs. 6
love with our praise.

Vs. 1,6
1. na - tion and race.
6. love with our praise.

Vs. 2-5
2. know when and where.
3. clash and for - give.
4. ef - forts should be.
5. lead and be led.

D.C.

Unison

1. Christ is the world's light; Christ and none oth - er; Born in our
2. Christ is the world's peace: Christ and none oth - er; No one can
3. Christ is the world's life, Christ and none oth - er; Sold once for
4. Give God the glo - ry, God and none oth - er; Give God the

dark - ness, he be - came our broth - er. If we have seen him,
serve him and de - spise an - oth - er. Who else u - nites us,
sil - ver, mur - dered here, our Broth - er— He, who re - deems us,
glo - ry, Spir - it, Son and Fa - ther; Give God the glo - ry,

we have seen the Fa - ther: Glo - ry to God on high!
one in God the Fa - ther? Glo - ry to God on high!
reigns with God the Fa - ther: Glo - ry to God on high!
God in Man my broth - er: Glo - ry to God on high!

WORDS: Fred Pratt Green
MUSIC: French Church Melody *Antiphoner*, Paris, 1681
Words Copyright © 1969 by Hope Publishing Company, Carol Stream, IL 60188. All Rights Reserved.

CHRISTE SANCTORUM
10 11.11 6.

128 Christ Be My Leader

Unison

1. Christ be my lead - er by night as by day; safe through the dark - ness, for he is the way. Glad - ly I fol - low, my fu - ture his care, dark - ness is day - light when Je - sus is there.

2. Christ be my teach - er in age as in youth, drift - ing or doubt - ing, for he is the truth. Grant me to trust him; though shift - ing as sand, doubt can - not daunt me; in Je - sus I stand.

3. Christ be my Sav - ior in calm as in strife; death can - not hold me, for he is the life. Nor dark - ness, nor doubt - ing, nor sin and its stain can touch my sal - va - tion: with Je - sus I reign.

WORDS: Timothy Dudley-Smith
MUSIC: Traditional Irish Melody, arr. by Donald P. Hustad

SLANE
10 10.10 10.

Jesus, Life of All the World 129

1. Je - sus, life of all the world, source and sum of
2. Life of free - dom, glad - ness, truth, all our guilt and
3. Yours is life that makes us stand firm for truth, all
4. Je - sus, life of all the world, you are Lord of

all cre - a - tion, Son of God and Son of Man,
fear trans - cend - ing: life that leaps be - yond the grave,
wrong de - fy - ing; yours the strength by which we strive,
ev - ery na - tion; by your Ho - ly Spir - it's power

on - ly hope of our sal - va - tion, Liv - ing
God's own life that knows no end - ing: life e -
on your ho - ly arm re - ly - ing: yours the
make your Church your in - car - na - tion till our

Word for all our need, life you give is life in deed:
ter - nal, gift un - priced, free - ly ours in Je - sus Christ!
war we wage on sin, yours the power by which we win.
lives of truth and grace show our world your hu - man face!

WORDS: Margaret Clarkson
MUSIC: Johann Crüger

JESUS, MEINE ZUVERSICHT
78.78.77.

130 May the Lord, Mighty God

May the Lord, might - y God, bless and

keep you for - ev - er; Grant you peace,

Fine

per - fect peace, cour - age in ev - ery en - deav - or.

Voice I

Lift up your eyes and see his face and his

Voice II

Lift up and see his face, his

grace for - ev - er; May the Lord,

grace for - ev - er; May the Lord,

D. C.

might - y God, bless and keep you for - ev - er.

D. C.

might - y God, bless and keep you for - ev - er.

WORDS: Anon., Psalm 29:11

MUSIC: Chinese Folk Song, probably by Pao-chen Li

WEN-TI

Irregular

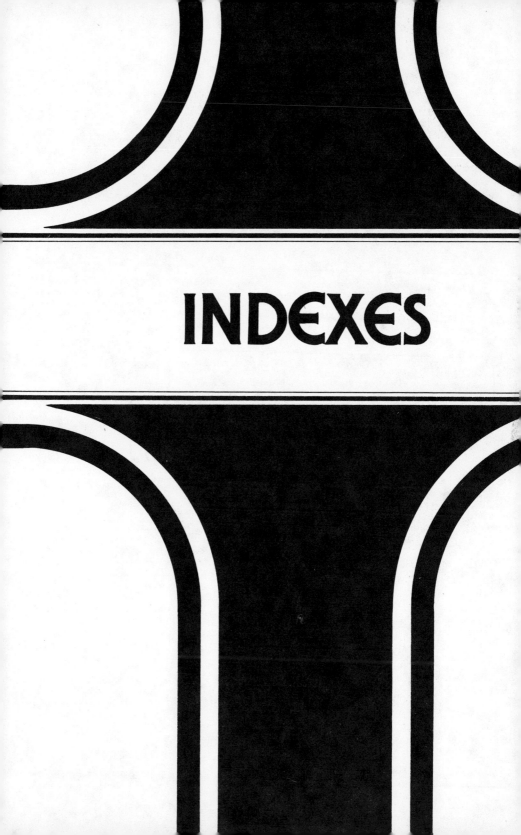

INDEXES

COPYRIGHT OWNERS

In the copyright notice when just the word "Copyright" is used, it applies to both words and music. If just the words are copyright, the notice will say "Words Copyright." If no other copyright notice appears, the music is in the Public Domain.

AGAPE (contact HOPE PUBLISHING COMPANY) Hymns 2, 4, 8, 11, 17, 20, 23, 24, 25, 26, 27, 31, 34, 40, 41, 43, 46, 47, 48, 52, 53, 56, 58, 69, 70, 71, 73, 76, 78, 79, 80, 85, 87, 89, 90, 93, 94, 98, 100, 104, 106, 107, 108, 110, 114, 115, 117, 118, 119, 123, 124.

A.P. WATT LTD., 26/28 Bedford Row, London WC1R 4HL, England—01 405 1057: Hymn 112.

AUGSBURG PUBLISHING HOUSE, 426 South Fifth Street, Box 1209, Minneapolis, MN 55440—(612) 330-3300: Hymns 61,62,92,95.

BAUGHEN, THE RT. REV. MICHAEL A., Bishop's House, Abbey Square, Chester, CH1 2JD, England: Hymns 60,65,109.

CARL FISCHER, INC., 62 Cooper Square, New York, NY 10003—(212) 777-0900: Hymn 96.

CHANTRY MUSIC PRESS, INC., Box 1101, Springfield, OH 45501: Hymn 37.

CHURCH PASTORAL AID SOCIETY, Falcon Court, 32 Fleet Street, London, EC4Y 1DB, England: Hymns 13,86,99.

CONCORDIA PUBLISHING HOUSE, 3558 S. Jefferson Ave., St. Louis, MO 63118—(314) 664-7000: Hymns 66,78.

CRAWFORD, MARY BABCOCK, 2884 Galleon Rd., Pebble Beach, CA 93953: Hymn 8.

EDITIONS DU CERF., 29 Blvd. de Latour, Maubourg, 75007 Paris, France: Hymn 112.

FABER MUSIC, 3 Queen Square, London, WC1N 3AU, England—01 278 6881: Hymn 123.

G. SCHIRMER, INC., 866 Third Ave., New York, NY 10022—(212) 935-5100: Hymn 68.

GALAXY MUSIC CORPORATION, 131 West 86th St., New York, NY 10024—(212) 874-2100: Hymns 82,84.

GARDNER, JOHN, 10 Lynton Road, New Malden, Surrey, KT3 5EE, England: Hymn 77.

G.I.A. PUBLICATIONS, INC., 7404 S. Mason Ave., Chicago, IL 60638—(312) 496-3800: Hymns 13,72,86,99.

GRAIL, THE (contact A.P. WATT LTD.) Hymn 112.

HINSHAW MUSIC, INC., P.O. Box 470, Chapel Hill, NC 27514—(919) 929-0337: Hymn 2.

HOPE PUBLISHING COMPANY, Carol Stream, IL 60188—(312) 665-3200: Hymns 1, 3, 5, 6, 7, 9, 10, 12, 13, 14, 15, 19, 21, 22, 23, 28, 30, 32, 33, 35, 36, 38, 39, 40, 42, 44, 45, 47, 49, 50, 51, 54, 55, 57, 59, 60, 63, 64, 65, 68, 72, 73, 75, 77, 79, 81, 82, 83, 84, 86, 88, 91, 95, 97, 99, 101, 102, 103, 105, 109, 111, 113, 115, 116, 120, 121, 122, 125, 126, 127, 128.

HYMNS ANCIENT & MODERN LIMITED, St. Mary's Works, St. Mary's Plain, Norwich, Norfolk, NR3 3BH, England—(0603) 612914: Hymn 67.

HYMN SOCIETY OF AMERICA, THE (contact HOPE PUBLISHING COMPANY) Hymns 16,29,62,74,92,129.

J. CURWEN & SONS (contact G. SCHIRMER, INC.) Hymn 68.

ORCHARD, THE REV. DR. STEPHEN, The British Council of Churches, 2 Eaton Gate, London, SW1W 9BL, England—01-730 9611: Hymn 59.

OXFORD UNIVERSITY PRESS, Ely House, 37 Dover Street, London, W1X 4AH, England—01-629 8494: Hymns 10,11,15,38,57,76,105,122.

PEACEY, MRS. M.E., 10 Park Cottages, Manor Road, Hurstpierpoint, West Sussex, BN6 9UW, England: Hymn 70.

WESTMINSTER PRESS, THE, 925 Chestnut St., Philadelphia, PA 19107—(215) 928-2700: Hymn 110.

WETZLER, ROBERT, c/o Art Masters Studios, Inc., 2614 Nicollet Ave., Minneapolis, MN 55408—(612) 872-8831: Hymn 18.

METRICAL INDEX

METRICAL INDEX

87.87.87.
All Saints, 45
Corbridge, 17
Fortunatus New, 78

87.87.87. with Refrain
Gloria Patri, 26

87.87.88.87.
God of Gods, 86

87.87.9.88.
Ilse, 111

885.86.
East Meads, 50

886.D.
Allgütiger Mein Preisgesang, 22

88.77.8. (Troch.)
The Church Within Us, 28

888.4.
Ripponden, 122

88.86. with Refrain
Christmas Peace, 31

88.88.88.
Farmborough, 93
Russwin, 72

97.97.
Uplifted Eyes, 65

97.97. with Refrain
Earth and All Stars, 61

98.96. with Refrain
The Beatitudes, 51

98.98.
Folksong, 38
Harvest, 123

98.98.D.
Rendez À Dieu, 41

9 10.10 9.
Althorp, 73

10 9.10 9.
Bunessan, 15

10 10.10 4.
Engelberg, 1

10 10.10 10.
Litton, 70
Slane, 128
Woodlands, 5

10 10.10 10. with Refrain
Crucifer, 67

10 10. 11 11.
Hanover, 108
Normandy, 2

10 11.10 11.
Circle, 85
Heartbeat, 56

10 11.11 6.
Christe Sanctorum, 127

11 10.11 10.
City of God, 62
Donne Secours, 74
Intercessor, 83
Lincoln, 100
Lord of the Years, 109

11 10.11 10. with Refrain
Faithfulness, 44

12 12.8 8.
Love Unknown, 113

12 12.12.
Acclamations, 7

15 15.15 7.
Heritage, 47

Irregular
Blantyre, 114
Chereponi, 4
Christ the Worker, 71
Clarence, 14
Collins, 35
Divinum Mysterium, 32
Feast, 18
Gelineau, 112
Glorious Coming, 60
Now, 19
Pathways, 117
Proclamation, 63
Quiet Understanding, 97
Rosechester, 64
Rowand, 116
Wen-Ti 130
Whitfield, 126
Wilcox, 101

TUNE NAME INDEX

AUTHORS, COMPOSERS AND SOURCES INDEX

AUTHORS, COMPOSERS AND SOURCES INDEX

TOPICAL INDEX

TOPICAL INDEX

Saints
O Paradise, 118

Worship and Praise of God
A new day bids us wake, 79
As the bridegroom to his chosen, 88
Christ is made the sure foundation, 20
Earth and all stars, 61
For the fruit of all creation, 95
Glory be to God the Father, 26
Glory be to the Father, 63
God is! Rejoice! 116
God of gods, 86
How wondrous great, 27
It is God who holds the nations, 47
Let us build a house of worship, 39
New songs of celebration render, 41
Praise God from whom all blessings, 103
Sing a new song to the Lord, 13
Thanks to God, 23

Holy Communion
An upper room did our Lord prepare, 38
As we break the bread, 46
Become to us the living bread, 110
Break the bread Jesus, 18
Here, O my Lord, 90
I come with joy, 40
Let us talents and tongues employ, 24
Now let us from this table rise, 43
Now the silence, 19
This is the threefold truth, 7

Baptism
O Jesus Christ, our Lord most dear, 106

Confirmation
All that Christians have in life, 104
You called me, Father, 29

Footwashing
An upper room did our Lord prepare, 38
Jesu, Jesu, fill us with your love, 4

Marriage
The grace of life is theirs, 113

CHRISTIAN EXPERIENCE AND DEVOTION

Consecration and Prayer
All who worship God in Jesus, 32
Breathe on me, breath of God, 80
By gracious powers, 83
Christ be my leader, 128
Forgive our sins as we forgive, 11
He turned to say "Come, follow me", 35
Jesu, Jesu, fill us with your love, 4
Jesus, life of all the world, 129
Lord, for the years, 109

Lord, let me love, 100
Lord, you give to us, 59
Love is your name, 52
May the mind of Christ my Saviour, 42
My dear Redeemer, 107
Open, Lord, my inward ear, 98
The grace of life is theirs, 113
Though I may speak with bravest fire, 30

Hope and Courage
A mighty fortress is our God, 66
God is hope, and God is now! 125
Hope of the world, 74
O Christ the Lord, 93
Out of our night of day, 87
Sometimes a light surprises, 96
We have heard it, we have seen it, 111
Weary of all trumpeting, 37

Family
Lord, you give to us, 59

CHRISTIAN CONCERNS AND SERVICE

All who love and serve your city, 84
Break not the circle, 85
Christ is alive! 81
For the healing of the nations, 78
Go forth for God, 70
God has set us free, 119
God, who stretched, the spangled, 6
God, whose giving knows no ending, 16
He turned to say, "Come follow me", 35
Help us accept each other, 89
How can we name a love, 115
How clear is our vocation, Lord, 36
Lord Christ, the Father's mighty Son, 50
Lord, let me love, 100
O God of every nation, 92
O God, whose will is life, 9
O Jesus Christ, to you may hymns, 62
Thank you, God, for water, soil and, 73
The Church of Christ, in every age, 54
We are your people, 126
We plow and sow with tractors, 102
We utter our cry, 108
Weary of all trumpeting, 37
When the church of Jesus, 57

PSALMS AND CANTICLES

My Shepherd is the Lord, 112
Tell out, my soul, 5

ALPHABETICAL INDEX OF HYMNS

ALPHABETICAL INDEX OF HYMNS